Pete Dec 89

THE CROSS OF

Dilemmas of a

To Jea & Len

The Cross of Unknowing

Dilemmas of a Catholic Doctor

Joyce Poole

Sheed & Ward
London

To Geoffrey

Indeed you love truth in the heart;
Then in the secret of my heart teach me wisdom.

Psalm 50

ISBN 0–7220–2850–4

Published in Great Britain in 1989 by
Sheed & Ward Limited
2, Creechurch Lane
London, EC3A 5AQ

Book production Bill Ireson

Filmset by Waveney Typesetters, Norwich
Printed and bound by BPCC Wheatons Ltd, Exeter

Contents

Preface

So many friends and one time colleagues have given freely of their time and specialised field of knowledge that it would be invidious to try to name them all. I hope they will accept this inclusive expression of my great indebtedness.

My particular thanks are due, however, to Dr Christopher Cameron who has read the manuscript with enthusiasm and meticulous care: his concern for sense and language has prevented many an inaccuracy or ambiguity. Any which remain are of course my own.

I sincerely thank too Mrs Celina Bullick whose intelligent deciphering of the manuscript and accurate typing have made the production of the book both a possibility and a pleasure.

Introduction

In the Western world the Catholic Church is seen by many to be in a state of decline which is approaching crisis. Priests are dying, or leaving the Church, in greater numbers than they are being ordained and the numbers of practising Catholic laity have fallen dramatically. Whatever the causes might be it is essential in such a setting that the truths which the Church proclaims and represents are not obscured by irrelevancies and inessentials. A Catholic is a person who finds Christ's continuing presence in the Church and its sacraments, rather than a member of a sect which has singular and often perplexing views on certain aspects of sexual and medical ethics.

This book is mainly about such non-essential issues and reflects on the fact that there is more than one way of looking at moral problems within the framework of sincere Christian conviction.

Whilst it is an accepted legal maxim that hard cases make bad law, it is my experience as a Catholic doctor that in the moral field, especially that of medical ethics, there is no general law so determinate that it can be applied with confidence to all particular cases; I fear, for those of us within the Church, that too much specific moral direction in this area by the Magisterium might endanger its credence and authority on more important matters central to its teaching. It would be a matter of great concern if we were to end up with a code of ethics which is out of touch with the body of the Church.

Within the Catholic Church nothing can have caused more widespread and unprecedented dismay than the publication on birth-control, *Humanae Vitae*. Since then, to those outside it, the image of the Church has been distorted by an apparent obsession with sexual ethics.

I came into the Church in the wake of the encyclical having

been many years on the way and after instruction from several priests of different backgrounds. I knew that I did not agree with the Church's stand on contraception and saw this as a possible though not central problem. In the event the subject was never mentioned. It seems that my instructors too regarded the matter as peripheral to the core of Catholic Christian belief.

A high and informed standard of ethical behaviour is not of course a Christian prerogative. It has been specifically demanded of physicians since the early Greeks and is enshrined both in the law and in the requirements of professional bodies such as the Royal Colleges and the General Medical Council.

Furthermore it is generally understood that Catholic and other Christian moral teaching relies on reason as well as authority and the churches have grown historically by learning from the prudent judgement of their members. In the past, pronouncements on subjects as diverse as Darwinism and slavery have had to be adjusted to keep pace with scientific and social progress.

When the teaching of the Church on ethical matters is out of tune with current human experience a real conflict is set up within many of those who would count themselves as committed Catholics. This conflict by its very nature cannot be resolved without sacrifice of either conviction or loyalty to the Magisterium.

It is the theme of these reflections that the best that many of us can do is to carry the burden of uncertainty willingly and if possible cheerfully as part of our human condition, trusting in the charity of those who misunderstand us and ultimately in God's grace and inexhaustible patience.

Reflections on Authority

We all like rules; in childhood indeed our security depends on them. The child of the overstrict parent may envy his friend whose mother is ever indulgent but both are immeasurably more fortunate than the one whose parents have no consistent rules at all – who is allowed to do something one day and not the next. We cannot grow up and mature, unfortunately, without leaving behind such childhood certainties, but the hankering remains. We like to know where we are. In illness and old age we see how quickly people become hospitalised and institutionalised; rules which were designed mainly for safety and smooth running are quickly seized upon by people too frail to be burdened with choice or responsibility.

In the Catholic Church, with a tradition of authority stronger than most, older people still remember wistfully their younger days when rules and sins were more clearly defined, and life was, or so it was thought, correspondingly easier. Rules offer a security which most people at times would prefer to responsibility but there is a danger of producing a person who in Mark Twain's words 'is good in the worst sense of the word'.

It must be right that the Second Vatican Council should have changed the focus.

> Every man has the duty and therefore the right to seek the truth in matters religious in order that he may, with prudence, form for himself right and true judgments of conscience with the use of all suitable means.[1]

> Conscience is the most secret core and sanctuary of a man. There he is alone with God . . . To obey his conscience is his very dignity: according to it he will be judged.[2]

All the faithful, clerical and lay possess a lawful freedom of enquiry and thought and the freedom to express their minds humbly and courageously about those matters in which they enjoy competence.[3]

In the Church of England, *The Family in Contemporary Society*, which was published as a report to the Lambeth Conference of Bishops, 1958, had applied the method of interdisciplinary study and discussion in such a way that

theological insights were allowed to illuminate and articulate the moral claim inherent in the subjects under discussion, without dictating prior conclusions.[4]

The churches seemed to be acknowledging that in a time of rapid advances in so many scientific fields they did not always have to hand the solution to all particular problems.

In the field of medical ethics such particular problems have increased exponentially since these documents were written. Reproductive techniques then unthought of have become attainable; the contraceptive pill has become easily obtainable and widely used; transplant surgery of vital organs is commonplace. Sophisticated resuscitative procedures for the desperately ill and for the grossly premature baby can no longer be included in the term 'extraordinary means' traditionally used by the Church. When, the practising doctor might ask, do the means required to keep someone alive become 'extraordinary', or when, for that matter, does a 'brain-dead' patient stop being 'someone', and, if the state of not-yet-being-someone exists and can be defined, should the embryo too be legitimately available for biological research in the service of others? The Catholic Church emphatically forbids the last, while most others, including the Church of England, are less certain.

Progress in reproductive techniques such as *in vitro* fertilisation and the understanding and overcoming of some of the commonest causes of infertility depend on the availability of spare embryos for research purposes. These include failure of the zygote to implant or develop further and the large problem of male infertility. This is widely accepted by the

2

other mainstream churches and by the public at large, and the Catholic Church, if it is to avoid the label of a sect, will have to define its position coherently and rationally rather than present it as a set of deeply-held convictions. The singling out by the Magisterium of the Catholic Church of moral issues concerned with sexual and reproductive functions has almost certainly caused more perplexity than any other for those both inside and outside its fold. Although many guidelines and indeed directives have been issued, there can be no field more than that of bio-ethics where the exceptional case so often presents itself, not so much as a matter for discussion between moral theologians but as a position to be taken in the face of urgent human problems. In the 1950s 'Situation Ethics' drew strong condemnation from Pope Pius XII. This has since been upheld, yet is not ethics intimately concerned with what to do when you are not sure what to do?[5] It is one thing in a doctrinal context to argue a case against, for example, contraception, by appeal to tradition and Natural Law, but quite another to refuse help, either clinically or pastorally, to a woman distraught with too much child bearing. Such a woman, as likely as not, will be incapable of understanding or applying so-called 'natural methods' and will probably have a husband who would not co-operate if she did. The Catholic doctor might have to choose between upholding the moral dogma of the Church and helping his patient. E. M. Forster famously remarked that if he had to choose between betraying his friend and betraying his country he hoped he would have the courage to betray his country.

Christianity is not a system of ethics though it adds another dimension to decision making. It will not tell us what to do, though belief and grace may increase our moral insight and enable us to see more clearly and act, if necessary, more courageously. A moral person in either the secular or Christian sense will have no real problem in deciding between good and bad. The difficulty is between good and good, or bad and bad, and most real moral problems in daily life fall into this category. They are as often as not about who is to get hurt and the injunction to love everybody does not help though it is frequently invoked by religious people. The trouble with 'Situation Ethics', of course, is that it does not really help where help is most needed. It is easier to agree to the Commandment to love one's neighbour, than to decide who that neighbour is. Religion is concerned with ultimate questions, and advances in medicine force it to question ultimate aims.[6] The two disciplines are traditionally associated from the Ancient World through Judaism and Christianity, but the principles of the first applied to the second do not necessarily lead to detailed conclusions reaching through the whole field of medical ethics and pastoral counselling. The Commandment to remember the Sabbath Day and keep it holy was to do with displacing work from the centre and making time and space for God; it had little to do with the minutiae of Jewish law in the time of Jesus Christ (who did not hesitate to say so) or with the austerities of Sunday in some of the Western Islands of Scotland. In the same way it seems probable that the Commandment 'Thou shalt not kill' should be interpreted not so much as a rule for the treatment of, say, the early embryo, as a directive to be *concerned* about killing whether directly and intentionally, or indirectly and unintentionally by poverty, famine or the pollution of the environment in the cause of profit and greed. If it is accepted that no principle of law, civil or ecclesiastical can possibly determine the values to be considered and balanced in every particular case we are thrown upon our own appraisal of the situation and an awareness of the touchstones in our lives which give a sense of what comes from God. We must be ready to accept that we may make a decision which involves the Cross – criticism, censure or worst, self-doubt.

The authority of the Magisterium of the Church in matters within its competence is not here being questioned but there is an authority too residing in those of us who have a lifetime of listening in close and frank contact to the problems of ordinary people. In the surgery or in the confessional after considering all the data, including the teaching of the Church, we may consider that ultimately three people matter – ourselves, God and the patient.

Some Reflections on Suffering

A senior nurse in the childrens' hospital where we had both worked for some years commented: 'No one could believe in God and work here.'

It was an acute surgical ward, and Christmas Day, which made the circumstances memorable. The 'up' children were singing carols and enjoying hilarious games while a little boy, admitted that day from a road accident, died quietly behind screens. We had to take off our party hats to attend to him. In an inconspicuous corner was a two-year-old girl with such appalling congenital facial deformities that an official visitor that morning had literally fainted at the sight of her. We were trying to improve surgically the worst of the girl's malformations, but she would provoke horror and pity for the rest of her life.

The paradox of an All Powerful yet All Loving God apparently passive in the face of human suffering, is to many people the main objection to Christian belief.[1] It would seem a choice would have to be made between all powerful and all loving, or more easily, to retreat altogether into agnosticism. Those, such as nurses, doctors and clergy, whose daily work brings them into intimate contact with suffering and death must perhaps, more urgently than most, come to a working philosophy of suffering in the context of their religious belief.

Does God actually *will* suffering? Many Christian people seem to believe, implicitly at least, that He does. 'It is hard to see God's will in this,' is frequently heard from religious people who have made the underlying assumption that their pain or bereavement is indeed the will of God, perplexing though it might be. Had the child dying behind the screens been 'called to a higher life', as would no doubt be said later by somebody at his funeral or had he simply been in the way of a car driver who had had too much to drink over Christmas? Had the one with the facial deformity been singled out in some way by a God who could see some ultimate good come out of it, or was she the victim of a chance throw of the genetic dice?

It has to be remembered of course that chance genetic variation can work for good and give us a Mozart or an Einstein, and it is almost certainly the mechanism of natural selection. If so, what is God's role as creator of all things, including the very substance of genes? These are big questions and although big answers will not be attempted here, an effort must be made if a working faith is to be woven into a working life, and if there is to be some kind of wholeness of outlook.

In this century advances in the basic sciences have demonstrated a chaos and apparent randomness in the realms of particle physics and biology; this is some distance removed from the comparatively simple cause-and-effect or 'clockwork' image of matter and the universe, which was the legacy of Newtonian physics. None the less there is a system, in the natural creation, of physical laws which remain constant and predictable and without which our experience of life would itself be chaotic. If one could not depend, say, on the unvarying operation of the laws of gravity, then walking, eating, digestion even would be difficult and safe landing of an airliner impossible. If a stone, obeying these constant laws falls from a high building and kills an unfortunate person in the street do we see it as God's direct will that it should fall just there, and if it is not, can He suspend that particular law momentarily 'like some Divine laser beam', as the Bishop of Durham puts it? If He can, and does not, it is hard to see Him as the loving Father of the Gospels, who cares for each one of us and for the sparrows too.

I attended a Lenten discussion group in another parish and the subject of Destiny came up one evening. All (except myself) considered that if I were to be killed in an accident on my way back they would see it as God's will that my life should end that night, that it would all be part of a divine plan. Had I shared this view and, driving home without care and attention killed some pedestrian in the street would that also have been seen as God's plan? What if the person had not been killed, but brain damaged, and suffered greatly for the rest of his life? The argument can be extended indefinitely, but in that direction lies madness, and surely could not lead to a Christian view of life. It is a kind of thinking common in wartime when people will say in an air-raid that a bomb will not fall on you unless it has your name on it. If it has, that's it. If it hasn't you are safe. It is a comfortable philosophy in times of danger, popular in the trenches of the First World War, but not easily credible.

What then of 'natural disasters' which undoubtedly cause suffering. If the crust of the Earth were of uniform thickness and density earthquakes as such would not occur and we should have no recurring disasters in places like Latin America, with pitiful children on our television screens. Earthquakes, like floods and plague are often listed by insurance companies as Acts of God. It is reasonable to postulate, however, that without geographically weak areas which can infold, the cooling planet would implode to dust, ending life on Earth altogether.

Bacteria, viruses and DNA molecules are part of a balanced ecology obeying biophysical laws within an orderly creation. Without bacteria to break down dead matter the Earth would be choked with dead things. If these bacteria, following their own intrinsic nature like the stone falling from the building, invade living tissue and cause disease, can we again expect God to intervene specifically in the ecological system and change the principles of cellular metabolism and reproduction on which our whole biological system depends? Death, it has been said, is a biological necessity, and God made creation the way it is.

Lead can be a deadly poison and has been shown beyond reasonable doubt to cause central nervous system damage in children who live in areas of high traffic density. This is surely our fault, when we fail so miserably to reduce the source of contamination rather than God's fault for making the essential leadishness of lead. Lead is 'good' when it is used as a shield against X-rays.

Malignant disease is an abnormality of cellular reproduction not yet fully understood though it is clear that it can be caused among other things by some irritants, some of which have been identified. It has been postulated that some degenerative diseases of the central nervous system may have an environmental factor: we are still, probably, at an early stage of human development in understanding, adapting to and protecting our environment.

What though of pain? Of course it is protective, warning us of disease and injury, but could not God have devised a less 'painful' method of protecting us? So often it appears to have no useful function. Once a bone is broken it seems a pity that it goes on hurting. The problem is that pain-carrying nerve fibres which we regard as 'good' when they warn us of trouble in a tooth are designed specifically to carry pain: if we demand that they transmit instead warm comfortable feelings it would be asking God to change their very nature, like asking lead not to act like lead when it gets into the nervous system, but to act dependably like lead when it is used as a screen to protect radiographers from harmful exposure to X-rays.

We have our God-given intelligence as well as the resources to prevent much suffering. We know more or less where earthquake zones are, where rainfall is likely to fail, where population growth is exceeding the food supply and how to prevent much disease. If we fail to apply our knowledge through lack of will or from material greed, it seems unfair to regard the resultant suffering as Acts of God. I doubt if prayers for rain in Ethiopia, however sincerely made, are ever *directly* answered, but God moves in mysterious ways and Bob Geldof was a kind of miracle. God seems to prefer to act through us.

When pain occurs, doctors are highly privileged in so often having the means to relieve it. Pain Clinics are being set up in most of the major hospitals and highly-sophisticated techniques for the relief of intractable pain such as can occur in bone, are being developed rapidly. The hospice movement with its expert management of terminal pain graces our society.

8

It is not denied for a moment, of course, that good can come out of suffering. People can rise to heroic heights in dealing with personal or social catastrophe, and thereby gain in spiritual growth and insight. At such times most of us hope for the loving support of family and friends and this can be the source of much of our strength. Those who love us suffer with us, not able to bear our pain physically, but suffering none the less. Daniel Berrigan, S.J., tells a moving story of his own near-death experience in a prison hospital. He asks himself afterwards if in this he had seen God's face. No, he had not, he thought, then on further reflection, yes he had, in the presence and anxious faces of those who loved him and upheld him in the long hours. Is this not what we ask of God?[2]

The centrality of a suffering God distinguishes Christianity from other mainstream religions. Can a transcendent God suffer? If Jesus Christ, God Incarnate as we believe, showed us what God was like, then suffering was part of His revelation. His Passion occurred at an historical point in time but that bit of God that we could see could be likened to the rings in the trunk of a tree,[3] visible only where they are exposed but running down to the roots of the past and into the branches of the future. The Incarnation showed us perhaps not only what God was like but enabled Him to know what it was like to be us: to suffer pain, fear, loneliness and abandonment not only by His friends but by the Father. 'My God, why hast Thou forsaken me?' Anything we go through, He has gone through. Of course God cannot share physical suffering with us now but the loving father-image is central to Christian belief. The suffering of a loving parent for his children is part of human experience. We create our children, love them and bring them up in accordance with our own principles: if they suffer physically, or hurt one another or 'let us down' we suffer for them and with them. The pain of anxiety about someone we love is hard to locate or to describe but we know it because we experience it.

'Clinical detachment' is often described as a virtue to be cultivated in doctors. I have reservations about this. Some self-discipline is necessary of course, for psychological health and to preserve the ability to carry on professionally, but I believe the good doctor must accept to some extent the burden of involvement. As Carl Rogers maintains he must go further than seeming to care: he must actually care.[4] To allow patients to share their suffering, fear and grief in this way is neither unrealistic nor self-righteous: it is no more than we are asked by God to do as members of His mystical body, His hands, His feet, His words. If we are aware of the presence of God in our daily work we can make emergency contact – Lord help me to be patient with this tiresome woman; help me to be calm in this alarming situation so that I may do my best. It doesn't always work: irritation may get the upper hand, and the desperately-ill patient may die but help has come in the asking. Clinical detachment has its place, of course, in another sense, and a very important one. The doctor or other professional carer must be able to withdraw when his services are no longer needed. Our ultimate aim is to help people to do without us.

Dr Robert Runcie translates Emmanuel Kant's 'wonder at the moral law within' less imposingly as 'wonder at the fact that things matter'.[5] To return to the nurse at the children's hospital. An awareness that things matter is present in most people even if it is unacknowledged and unexpressed and whether or not they subscribe to a formal religious belief: it is almost certainly the basis of the human ability to work and survive in the face of great suffering and overwhelming adversity.

Contraception

However much it may idealise family life there seems to be little doubt that the Church has a considerable distaste for sex.

The association of women with uncleanliness of course predates Christianity and has been a facet of many cultures, including that of the Jews in the time of Jesus Christ. Strict rules were devised for the segregation of menstruating women within the family and within society. The woman in Mark's Gospel who had an issue of blood for twelve years was suffering from more than her bleeding: she was also a social outcast and unclean. Schoolgirls still refer to 'The Curse' and the Church of England had until fairly recently at least, a service for the 'Churching' of women after childbirth, liturgically a thanksgiving, but more often regarded by the people as a kind of ritual cleansing before being received back into the Christian community. One of my grandmothers (both of them devout Protestants) would not partake of Holy Communion when she was menstruating and the other would not make jam or butter as she believed that they would not keep.

If the traditional Christian view of women and sexuality has its roots in the Genesis account of Adam and Eve the theology of sexual activity as sinful was developed by Paul who wrote: 'I see in my members another law at war with the law of my mind and making me captive to the law of sin which dwells in my members' (Romans 7:23).

Three centuries later St Augustine showed a similar disgust which has coloured church thinking ever since. It is recorded that at his conversion in 386 when he heard a divine voice directing him to the Scriptures he at once lighted upon the passage 'but put ye on the Lord Jesus Christ and make not provision for the flesh and the lusts thereof'. Although it was he who articulated the classic moral principle that a good end never justified evil means, he writes, on the question of sexuality 'he who has lawful intercourse through shameful lust is putting evil to good use', and 'what father would agree to hand his daughter over to the lust of another man were it not for children?'[1] If lawful marital sexual activity was considered in this light it is not difficult to see how the church's teaching on contraception evolved – the sin without the excuse. The procreation of children was the only possible justification for indulging in an activity which was at best, a distasteful duty and at worst, disgusting.

This distaste for sexuality almost certainly underlies the church's elevation of the state of virginity and priestly celibacy. The insistence on the perpetual virginity of Mary is a point of difference between the Roman and the Orthodox Churches. The Protestant Churches do not seem to worry about it one way or the other. On a visit to Jerusalem I heard an Armenian Christian guide refer to James, 'brother of Our Lord' as the founder of his Church. The following day another guide, presumably Roman Catholic, declared that these people were clearly greatly in error as it is known, 'as a fact', that Mary was ever virgin. In his opinion, therefore, their Church was built on a false premise making any thought of future intercommunion out of the question.

In the second century the Book of James elaborated various versions of the early life of Mary. One theory was that she was the second wife of Joseph, having been previously his ward. James, by this reckoning could have been an earthly 'half' brother of Jesus, a tortuous compromise perhaps but one which underlines the intrinsic value attached by the Church to physical virginity and unfortunately obscures the deep *theological* significance of the virginal conception of Jesus.

Celibacy can be strongly defended of course on grounds other than the negative virtue of sexual continence. The word is given two shades of meaning in the *Oxford Dictionary*: to refrain from sexual activity; and to live unmarried. The second aspect frees the priest and religious from all the secondary consequences of the married state – the provision of shelter, food and education for wife and children and from the social complications of an extended family – no Mrs Proudie need upset the life of the celibate cleric. This makes possible an immensely valuable gift to the life of the Church in the form of freedom and singleminded devotion to the service of God. Cardinal Hume put it vividly and simply on a television programme. He was spending Saturday evening at a youth club in his diocese and one of the children asked him why he wasn't married. 'Well,' he said, 'if I were married I would want to be spending the evening at home with my wife and family, and instead I am here, with you.'

The ban on contraception within marriage was dropped by the Bishops of the Church of England in 1930 but continues in the Catholic Church. In 1967 the reaffirmation of this traditional doctrine by Pope Paul VI in the encyclical *Humanae Vitae* burst upon the post-conciliar Church like a bombshell. Many, if not most, ordinary Catholics in those heady years had thought that they could consign the Church's teaching on birth-control to a place in history. In the often over-large Catholic families of their youth the constant anxiety about yet another pregnancy has been a nightmare which mothers did not want their daughters to inherit. There had been so much lightening of the load of traditional doctrines about Sins and Hell that the condemnation of birth-control had been presumed by many to have gone too.

Catholics had already been cleared for the 'rhythm' method of contraception. This effectively allowed separation of the marital act from the purpose of procreation so denying the very core of the Church's teaching, namely, that human intercourse should always be open to the transmission of life. Catholics who use the 'safe period' do so precisely because they hope such transmission will not be so. Many people thereafter found it hard to see any difference in *principle* between one method of birth-control and another. The contraceptive pill had, moreover, been generally understood to have been within a hair's breadth of acceptance by Rome.

I think it is accepted that many left the Church for good, no longer able to equate its teaching on this issue with the realities of their own daily lives and moral judgement. Most of those who remained seemed to have decided to follow their own conscience in this matter while remaining faithful to what they considered to be the Church's central doctrines. They saw the minutiae of the teaching on birth-control by the Magisterium in Rome as an intrusion and an unseemly irrelevance.

I happened to be in the United States when the disciplinary moves against Charles Curran came to a head and was interested and surprised at the amount of coverage given to it by the media. It is easy to forget when in Britain, how many Catholics there are in the United States and how much prominence is given in their press and television to Catholic affairs. Programme followed programme with interviews and discussion and it was very clear what the American Catholic laity thought. Fr Curran, at least on the contraceptive issue, was expressing the views already held and followed by the huge majority. As with us in Britain, I suspect most of them had regarded the issue as long since dead.

As a Catholic doctor I have had a close and privileged view of Catholic thinking on contraception over many years. In this time the clinical scene has changed completely. Catholic patients were first coming to ask for the Pill because they had heard it 'regulated the periods'. I would agree that this was so and would explain the mechanism and pharmacology. The word contraception hung between us unsaid; the principle of Double Effect is a well recognised one in Catholic moral theology. The original oestrogenic Pill acted by suppressing ovulation completely. There was, as a result of this suppression less build-up of the endometrial lining of the uterus: the subsequent 'period' (which is in reality withdrawal bleeding) was regular, slight and usually painless, making it a valuable and recognised treatment for heavy bleeding or period pains. In the absence of medical contraindication the decision would be made by the patient to try it and so the little deception would be innocently established between us and continued over the years. One Catholic patient told me with unconscious humour that she was 'taking it religiously'.

Some of the later, predominantly progestogenic Pills do not interfere with ovulation but act by making the cervical mucus impenetrable to sperm and the endometrium inimicable to implantation should fertilisation, by any chance, occur. This last possibility has led to the charge that such Pills are potentially abortifacient which, in a narrow sense, is patently true. In practice, those Catholic doctors who hold this view and are vehemently opposed to this type of Pill are unlikely in any case to be prescribing any form of contraceptive, while those Catholic patients who come for contraceptive advice are in my experience, either uninterested in or unconcerned about the differentiation. Believing that patients should be treated as responsible people I would try to explain, as far as it could be explained and understood, the mode of action of any drug prescribed whether it was for contraception or cardiac failure; in this matter, however, patients had for the most part already made up their minds.

In the early years the Pill for contraceptive purposes had to be given as a private prescription and paid for, while if it was for strictly medical reasons such as excessive or painful menstrual bleeding it could be prescribed on an NHS form like any other medicine. Which prescription form to use was often a difficult decision affecting the patient's sensibilities more importantly than her purse. It was a minefield through which one just had to pick one's way using tact and empathy rather than the rule book. Over the next fifteen years the picture changed completely. Many patients who were pillars of the Church, bringing up their children in the Faith, helping with parish activities, would come and ask straight out for the Pill or for other contraceptive advice. It was tacitly assumed that I, as a Catholic doctor, would have no hesitation in advising on the matter.

I too, of course, had read *Humanae Vitae*, and understood, and indeed shared Pope Paul's disquiet at the effect of too-easily available contraception. The easier sexual morality which has become the norm would seem at first sight to bear witness to his perception, yet I am unconvinced that the two are so clearly related. Historically and geographically sexual behaviour has varied enormously from one generation to another and one class or culture to another quite independently of contraceptive availability. Consider only that girls are reaching the menarche earlier than did their mothers and grandmothers while at the same time schooling has extended further into their teens. Girls and boys who have reached puberty in the first or second year of secondary school are still behind their desks when sexuality is at its height. Let us remember that Romeo and Juliet were fourteen. Social mores too, be it sex, alcohol or smoking are hugely influenced by the media which are now penetrating our lives on an unprecedented scale.

It would seem that moral, social and psychological attitudes have more bearing on extra-marital sexual activity than the availability of effective contraception. This activity, however, is not necessarily promiscuous. In Britain, one study has shown that three-fifths of the sexually experienced questioned had only ever had one partner and half of those who had had intercourse intended to marry their partner.[2] My own experience indicates that in a rural area where the standard of living is quite high and free from inner-city anonymity, schoolgirls are by no means queuing up for contraceptive advice. Nevertheless, there are some, but invariably they are those who are already leading an active sexual life and risking a pregnancy, usually to their 'steady boy-friend'. If they can be persuaded to come back together by appointment at the end of normal surgery hours and if they are treated seriously and responsibly and given time, they can often be dissuaded from continuing on a course which at its most basic level could involve them in a criminal charge if the girl is under sixteen years. This possibility is often one they have never thought of, so blinded are they by their romantic notions. The girls are usually interested too, in the possible long-term effects of taking a contraceptive pill in the mid-teens before an ovulatory pattern has been fully established. The spectre of future infertility can be powerfully persuasive. It is, after all, the more responsible of these young people who are consulting their family doctor in the first place. As a doctor I would not consider informing their parents, even if, as a mother, I can at least understand the sincere concern of those who disagree.

Occasionally a really promiscuous girl is referred by a social worker or the police and it has seemed to me that avoidance of a pregnancy is the most urgent consideration in such a case. It hardly needs to be said that I am not happy about prescribing the Pill for schoolgirls for medical as well as moral reasons, but I would consider it preferable to a disastrous pregnancy.

The vast majority of patients seeking contraceptive advice are, of course, not in that category at all but are married women wanting to space and then limit their families. In an area where Catholics are, admittedly, in a minority, there has been no observable difference in behaviour between Catholics and non-Catholics in this matter. A glance round Catholic churches up and down the country reveals pews containing families of only average size so I cannot think that my experience is unusual.

The contraceptive pill has been considered first as it requires the co-operation of a doctor. Condoms are easily obtainable across the counter and the new risk of AIDS has made their acquisition no longer an occasion for embarrassment. I myself was a long time married before it dawned upon me that the barber's archetypal question, 'Will there be anything else, sir?' referred to condoms. (It occurred to me while listening to Figaro.) Now one sees them at the checkout of many supermarkets.

It must be said, of course, that to observe is not necessarily to approve. None of the mainstream churches condones sexual promiscuity and all urge control and self-restraint at least outside marriage as being most in accord with human dignity and Christian ideals. It is well to remember, however, that the Catholic Church, while fully sharing these views also has a high tradition of realistic recognition of human frailty.

The intra-uterine device (IUD), like the Pill requires medical co-operation, usually from a gynaecological or family planning clinic. It acts as a foreign body in the cavity of the uterus and discourages implantation of a fertilised ovum. If, as in the teaching of the Catholic Church, the conceptus is regarded as having the right to be protected from the moment of fertilisation, the device is doubly condemned as contraceptive and abortifacient. Most Protestant churches, including the Anglican Church do not share this view and do not, therefore, condemn the method as intrinsically evil. In my experience the device has never been highly popular but on medical rather than on moral grounds. Many users bleed heavily and irregularly; the periods are often painful; it is often extruded; pelvic infection may occur; the failure rate varies with the type of device inserted, but it is for most people unacceptably high. Pelvic infection has always been a well-recognised danger and even when these devices were more popular few gynaecologists would recommend them for a woman who had not yet borne children. Certain types which had a woven rather than filamentous nylon thread acted like a wick drawing infection up into the uterus and uterine tubes. There is currently a considerable amount of litigation on that score in the United States initiated by women who have suffered consequent sterility. The simplicity of insertion has made them popular in some Third World countries where the risks attached to their use may be balanced against the risks of high multiparity and extreme poverty.

So where, it is legitimate to ask, does the Catholic doctor stand? If it is morally wrong to use a contraceptive it must be morally wrong to prescribe one, but the Catholic Church's prohibition of artificial contraception is based on an appreciation of that same Natural Law by which we all derive our innate moral sense. Contraception, at least within marriage, simply does not *feel* like a sin to large numbers of people who have decided none the less, to remain within the Church. If, as the Pope assures us, the teaching of *Humanae Vitae* 'is written by the creative hand of God in the nature of the human person' it might be wondered why so many of us are unaware of it.

Like many family doctors I have been prepared to teach the rhythm method approved by the Magisterium. Temperature and cervical mucus charts have been freely available as well as the time necessary to explain their use. They have been much in demand by women anxious to achieve a pregnancy but hardly at all by those who wish to avoid one. Those who embark on what they see as responsible family planning seek something wholly reliable, and, further, do not see anything particularly 'natural' in the daily recording of body temperature and the viscosity of the cervical mucus.

Both the short- and long-term side-effects of the contraceptive pill are so widely reported in the general press that with an increasingly well-informed laity we have people who have themselves weighed up the acceptable risks and advantages before coming for advice. The Pill has, of course, in addition to its perceived simplicity and reliability an enormous aesthetic advantage over all other methods. The taking of it is separated from the context in which it acts and furthermore it is in the hands of the woman which is a very important consideration in many marriages.

It would be appropriate at this point to consider in regard to contraception the position of the Catholic parish priest who, if normally observant, cannot have failed to notice that young married couples in his parish are limiting the size of their families. Nevertheless a homily on the subject is rarely heard and it seems to be their common experience that women simply do not mention the subject. If a woman comes for confession or help with a spiritual problem they do not ask, as she rises to go, if she is on the Pill. It seems that many seminarians who are well aware of the moral dogma of the Church on contraception simply put the matter aside. An outsider observing the Catholic Church could be forgiven for thinking that sexual ethics was its obsession. Instead, at ground level he would find silence. The dilemma of the hierarchy may seem to many to be as unreal as the emperor's new clothes. It is plain that contraception is being practised throughout the Church whether the Bishops and Magisterium accept it or not. This cannot be good for the health of the Church and the evasion and dishonesty it breeds is potentially highly destructive.

The issue is much more than an intellectual exercise in the application of Natural Law and magisterial authority to married life. An obsession with calendar watching, temperature taking and daily examination of the cervical mucus could become an anxious ritual which threatened to displace from the centre those great issues of family life which the Church so rightly wishes to nourish. Marital stability, the good relations which come from mutual tolerance, respect and loving kindness between parents and children are not easily achieved and require an input of energy which is drained by chronic anxiety. It is hard to avoid the suspicion that the Catholic Church in particular may regard a certain amount of anxiety in sexual matters to be not altogether a bad thing, as a 'forgiveness', in Augustinian language, for what might otherwise be unmitigated sexual enjoyment by married couples.

Those, on the other hand, who have made a study of marriage tend to see the sexual bonding between husband and wife as something in itself good which will outlast the reproductive years and help innocently to sustain the mutual comfort which man and wife seek to find in one another.

> Given the central role of the family in society and in Christian thought, the massive increase in marital breakdown is the single most serious social evil of Western society.[3]

The pain for the couples involved is severe and the consequences for the children disastrous. I share the anxiety of some, perhaps many, Catholic doctors that if the Catholic Church continues to focus so predominantly and specifically on purely sexual matters, it will be in danger of losing credence and authority on the wider aspects of human relations within marriage and the family.

IV

Sterilisation

There is no doubt that the advent of the contraceptive Pill caused a revolution in the attitude of women to their fertility which for the first time had come completely under their own control. Other contraceptives had been used for hundreds of years but there had been nothing which was at the same time both reliable and aesthetically acceptable. Women were eager to take the responsibility into their own hands and no longer accepted the probability of having more children than they felt they could reasonably manage.

Those who see no ethical objection to family planning within marriage almost invariably opt for a method that is primarily reliable even in the early years when it is used for spacing only. If so, once the family is regarded as complete, only two real alternatives remain: to continue with the Pill, perhaps for another twenty years or to consider sterilisation.

Those Christian Churches which do not prohibit artificial contraception – that is almost all the Protestant Churches including the Churches of England and Scotland – do not prohibit surgical sterilisation either. The total meaning of an act defines its morality and they regard it, insofar as they express a view at all, not as self-mutilation but as an extension of responsible family planning. All churches would agree of course that the decision to limit the number of children should be based on Christian charity, namely some larger good accomplished by family limitation. This good need not be pressing and urgent as in the case of abject poverty, or seriously threatened maternal health, but could be simply the perceived good of having only as many children as the parents consider they can rear and educate to the standard they have set for themselves: nor need this standard be a materialistic one, though it is often regarded as

21

such by those opposed in principle to family limitation by any artificial means.

In the First World there has been a dramatic drop in infant mortality in the last forty years. Before this, and within my own memory, childhood deaths were fairly common from respiratory infections, rheumatic heart disease and tuberculosis to name only a few. The advent of penicillin and other antibiotics and the development of immunisation procedures have changed the picture dramatically. A child death outside the peri-natal period (when prematurity and congenital abnormality still take their toll) is now thankfully uncommon so that a decision to regard a family as complete can be taken with relative confidence.

In Victorian England and in many Third World countries now, a high birth rate was seen as necessary both for the continuance of the family and as an economic necessity. Old graveyards bear testimony to the frequency of death in early childhood.

It is outside the scope of this book to consider world population problems but there is an increasing awareness of the needs of the dramatically rising world population which could outstrip the available natural resources to sustain them. Many thoughtful scientists see ecological disaster as the main threat to life on Earth, and that not too far distant.

To return to our brief: typically, a married couple in their thirties, children now at school, and who have used the Pill to space them, decide they are extremely unlikely to want to have any more. The mother may want to take up part-time work or to return to a professional career or simply want to have more time to enjoy and befriend both them and her husband as the family grows up. The choice, if they want to be certain lies between continuing with the Pill until the menopause has been reached or considering sterilisation.

A good deal of careful research has been done on the side effects of the contraceptive pill. Thrombo-embolic disease is the best known of these, not only to the medical profession but to the public at large. The risks obviously increase the longer the Pill is taken and are thought to be greater in the higher age groups. Women in their forties with a grown-up family who are usually those most anxious to avoid a further pregnancy are therefore at the greatest risk. For this reason it is becoming increasingly common to seek sterilisation: in most areas this is freely available and indeed encouraged on medical grounds by doctors and gynaecologists.

The choice then remains as to which of the married partners has the operation and this is a decision almost invariably left for them to decide for themselves unless for pressing medical considerations. Many woman see fertility control as their problem and choose to have the operation themselves. It involves usually a thirty-six hour admission to hospital and a general anaesthetic: through a laparoscope the uterine tubes are visualised and occluded with plastic clamps, a method preferred by most surgeons to diathermy which occasionally injures bowel or bladder. The abdominal incision is tiny and the woman is rarely uncomfortable for more than a week. The procedure takes effect immediately.

Many husbands, in increasing numbers in my experience, feel, on the contrary, that sterilisation is their responsibility and, wishing to spare their wives surgery, decide on vasectomy. This is also freely available in most areas and is usually done as an out-patient 'Day Case'. It can be done under either local or general anaesthetic depending on the patient and surgeon's choice and judgement. The technique is simple and involves dividing the vas deferens on both sides. Some post-operative discomfort is usual but most men require only a day off work. It takes two to three months to become effective as some viable sperm can remain in the bulbo-urethral gland: two negative sperm counts are therefore recommended before other contraceptive measures can be safely discontinued.

One frequently mentioned drawback after sterilisation of either partner is that after stopping the Pill the woman's periods revert to their normal pattern and may be both heavy and painful. A woman who has been accustomed to slight and painless bleeding while on the Pill sometimes finds this unacceptable and may come to hysterectomy some years later if the symptoms are severe. She would of course have come to this anyway – there is no evidence that taking the Pill for a number of years in any way affects the subsequent menstrual pattern. Apart from this eventuality the menopause is reached in due course in the normal way.

The operation does not affect libido in either man or woman and while psychological problems of inadequacy are very common in infertile men these have not been seen after voluntary sterilisation.

The slight but still significant risk of a general anaesthetic has to be pointed out and considered by the patient but the usual view taken is that both pregnancy and the Pill have inherent dangers which more than counterbalance the one-off risk of modern anaesthesia. Future 'peace of mind' is usually given as the overriding factor to be considered.

The possibility of future regret has to be carefully pointed out especially in the younger age group. With as many as one in three marriages ending in divorce this factor is highly significant and must always be considered before any decisions are taken. In my experience it is, interestingly, rarely regarded as important by those seeking sterilisation who have, typically, been married for eight to ten years and have school-age children. They are probably the most stable marital group in society as the divorce rate is highest in the first five years of marriage and peaks again after twenty when the children are grown up.

Most women take the view that they would not want to add to their family even if, or perhaps especially if, they were to lose their husband through death or separation. Sometimes a happily married woman will choose to have the operation herself because in the event of her death, she would hope her husband would marry again. This kind of generosity is quite common.

In an area where both male and female sterilisation is common practice I have not personally met a person who has regretted it, though it must occur. In either case while reversal may be attempted it is difficult and the operation should never be performed unless a patient understands this.

The following patient required reassurance about the permanent effect of the procedure.

A woman came to the area having been sterilised elsewhere at her own request in her early twenties after the birth of a second mentally-handicapped baby. Her teenage marriage had subsequently broken down and she had the custody of the children. In her thirties she wished to remarry and came to see me, not to ask if an attempt might be made to reverse her sterilisation but to be re-assured that it 'would still work'. A genetic abnormality had not been demonstrated in either her or her children although it was quite possibly present and deriving from her first husband. Both she and her prospective husband felt able to cope with her two handicapped children, but not with a third child of their own, even if it were to be born healthy. They remained happily married and the children of the first marriage were loved and well cared for.

The operation was not always so readily requested as the following cases illustrate.

An older woman came many years ago, when female sterilisation was uncommon, though legal in certain circumstances. It involved an abdominal incision and at least a week in hospital. She and her husband were in their late thirties and had two teenage children with Down's Syndrome. They had had genetic counselling and had been advised that the chances of a third were one in two. The children were marvellously cared for and both parents felt that their interests would be prejudiced by the arrival of another child even if it were to be born healthy. The mother was not keen to take the Pill in view of her age and additionally she had a raised blood pressure which is a medical bar: prolonged anxiety about another pregnancy was threatening the happiness of the whole family. She was referred to a gynaecologist who performed tubal ligation without hesitation.

An immigrant Irish Catholic in her mid-thirties was poor, and worn out with eight children and sundry miscarriages. She looked a good ten years older than her actual age. After her last baby which had to be delivered in a specialised maternity unit because of the dangers of high multiparity she told me she was desperate but would not consider the Pill or any other contraceptive for religious reasons.

We talked about the rhythm method but she found it complicated and in any case her husband though a kindly man was a weekend drinker and could not be counted on to co-operate. Additionally the Billings method is particularly unreliable in a woman of high multiparity as the cervix is often scarred and infected, and this alters the appearance and viscosity of the cervical mucus. She had an idea that it was possible to get permission for sterilisation if medical circumstances justified it and pleaded with me to 'write to the Bishop'. With considerable temerity I did so and received a very kind but of course negative reply. It could not have been otherwise in the immediate aftermath, for such it was, of *Humanae Vitae*.

She had heavy periods and as blood examination showed her to be moderately anaemic, I referred her to a gynaecologist hoping he would suggest hysterectomy. This he did, so solving many problems at once without transgressing her religious scruples. She was very grateful and tackled her other family problems with new heart.

The following case was my only instance of referring an unmarried person for sterilisation.

A 25-year-old girl was engaged to be married and came with her fiancé. She had a strong family history of Huntingdon's Chorea, her grandmother having died of it and her father and an aunt being severely affected.

Huntingdon's Chorea is a fearsome disease which usually manifests itself in the mid-forties by muscular incoordination and uncontrollable involuntary movements; this is usually followed by severe mental deterioration. Both her father and aunt were in long-term psychiatric institutions. Recent advances have identified the actual gene but at this time it was known simply to be a dominant. This meant the girl had a 50:50 chance of carrying it and therefore of developing the disease herself in middle life and of passing it on to her children in the meanwhile.

She wanted to get married but took the responsible decision not to have children. The man knew that his wife might develop the disease but was willing to take the risk and face the consequences. Adoption societies would not have considered them with this family history. They discussed the whole problem fully and courageously decided to go ahead with sterilisation.

Only one of the four patients quoted above had a 'religious' problem although all four were practising Christians.

Had the last patient been Catholic and followed the teaching of the Church her only real option would have been celibacy, both artificial contraception and sterilisation being forbidden. In the gravity of the circumstances natural contraceptive methods would have been an irresponsible choice because of their limited reliability. Many Christian decisions involve the Cross and this girl and her husband did in fact shoulder the burden of voluntary childlessness in a very admirable way. It would seem to many to be hard to deny them the comfort and support of marriage.

A very different and difficult problem attracted a great deal of attention in Britain during 1987. Permission was sought by a social work department in a Ward of Court proceeding to sterilise a 17-year-old mentally-handicapped epileptic girl, referred to in reports as 'Jeanette'. In the event, permission to sterilise was given, the judge having found that it was to be performed in the girl's best interests. It was emphasised that such authorisation should be exercised only as a last resort and that neither parent nor social work department could apply for a sterilisation operation without leave of the court in wardship proceedings.[1]

Those who remember the atrocities of Nazi Germany will recoil in horror from anything which smacks of eugenics but if that immediate response can be laid aside for a moment, it could be worthwhile to consider the circumstances of the 'Jeanette' case.

The present policy with regard to mentally-handicapped adults who have been in an institution is to return as many of them as possible to a more normal environment within the community. This seems to be rightly motivated and humane provided adequate funds and housing are made available. In the absence of a real family it often means patients living in small groups under the supervision of a house-parent or a specially trained team of social workers. One or two of the more able patients manage quite well on their own in sheltered housing. They are encouraged to live, within their limits, as full a life as possible, handling their own money and doing simple shopping.

'Jeanette' was reported as having the mind of a child of about five in a mature adult body. She enjoyed going out with friends and was encouraged to do so within the bounds of common sense. Groups of similarly handicapped people met, to my knowledge, for a weekly social gathering in a local pub mixing very successfully with members of the general community. It must be accepted that this policy almost inevitably exposes a young mentally-handicapped woman to the possibility of sexual abuse. It could be quite impossible to reconcile the object of making life enjoyable and normal for mentally-handicapped adults with the strict 24-hour supervision which was advocated by those who were most vehemently opposed to the idea of sterilisation. Even at home within a family such intense supervision may not be desirable.

The 20-year-old son of a patient of mine, severely mentally handicapped, was encouraged to fetch the daily paper: being a sociable character he often took his time over looking in on friends on his way home. He was part of the community. His mother admitted to being on edge until he was back but she thought it right not to curtail this morning routine which gave him such pleasure. It would certainly seem to be a more generous and unselfish thing that she suffered that daily anxiety than that she should have chosen the easier option of accompanying him wherever he went. Constant supervision can be both stifling and self-defeating. Nearly all able-bodied mentally-handicapped people take great pleasure in going out by themselves to a shop or to post a letter.

'Jeanette' lacked the understanding to give permission for any kind of operation or even medication. Had she, by great misfortune, become pregnant the social work department which was responsible for her would have been almost certain to present on her behalf a case for termination on grounds of the probability of severe psychological damage. Such a termination would necessarily have been without her consent, and the judge took account of this in the court hearing.

The object of concern in such a case is not the good of society or race, but the protection of a highly vulnerable person from a trauma they are not equipped to handle. 'Eugenics' does not come into it. Mental handicap itself is tragic. It is not being suggested that sterilisation ever could or should become a general policy: such an idea is repulsive. There might be an occasion, however, for a particular person in a particular situation, when it is the least harmful option when nothing by its very nature is ideal.

In ordinary family practice my experience of Catholic patients since the Second Vatican Council is that those who see their use of contraceptives as a private matter of conscience and one which is no ban to a continuing life in the Church, take the same view of sterilisation. They respect the right of their priest to the privacy of his own views on the matter and tend not to put him into the awkward position of having to declare them. Nor do they embarrass him by disclosing their own opinions in his presence, either publicly or privately: there is a discreet silence over the whole issue.

The decision to limit family size is, of course, not disapproved of basically by the Catholic Church. Fertility control is seen indeed by most Churches as a Christian responsibility. The difference between the Churches is *how*, and *how* is seen by many Catholics as a question considerably distanced from the core of faith.

They, like many other sincere Christian believers do not see their physical marital union in any way as a base or selfish sex drive and consider it unfitting that it should be subjected to metaphysical scrutiny and intrusive and detailed magisterial direction. The 'natural' method of contraception allowed by the Church of Rome is to some extent approved as 'natural' because it does not interfere with the marital act itself, but it may be pointed out that neither the Pill nor sterilisation offer any difficulty on this score; nor is coitus forbidden by the Church in pregnancy, during lactation, after hysterectomy or after the menopause, in none of which circumstances is it open to the creation of life.

For many couples the happiest time in their sexual lives is precisely after they consider their childbearing years to be over and they are enjoying the mutual comfort and companionship which is equally important in married life to the procreation of children. The demonstration of affection guarded for fear of pregnancy can be destructive to a marriage and provides fertile ground for the seeds of resentment and misunderstanding. Marriage is already a difficult undertaking as the breakdown rate clearly demonstrates.

Furthermore, Man and his morality must be seen in his social context. Abraham was not seen as a bigamist in his time. In our time, a long period of non-procreative sexual life is part of our normal marital pattern and, worldwide, may be considered to be biologically necessary. The consideration of the wisdom of this and how it can be best achieved should not be outside the sphere of influence of the Church, but the Church in its turn might do well to call on the wisdom of all the faithful, married and unmarried, clerical and lay to contribute their judgement and to speak with authority in those fields in which they have knowledge and experience.

The Status of the Embryo

While agreeing on the basic tenet of the sanctity of human life, the mainstream Christian Churches in Britain vary in the degree of human right they would accord to the fertilised ovum.

The Roman Catholic Church in its *Declaration on Abortion* (1974) is unequivocal. It declared

> that it is not for the biological sciences to pass a definitive judgement in questions which are properly moral or philosophical such as that of the moment when the human person first exists or of the liceity of abortion. From the moral point of view it is clear that even if there be some doubt whether the entity conceived is already a human person, it is an objectively serious sin to expose oneself to the danger of committing murder. He who will be a human being is already a human being . . . neither divine law nor human reason admit the right of directly killing an innocent person.[1]

It is to be noted that the Church does not claim in this statement that there *is* a human person from the time of conception but that it does not know, the matter being intrinsically unknowable. Attempts have been made over the centuries in the fields of philosophy, theology and medicine, to define this time of animation but with varying conclusions. Augustine, while aware of the seeming moral difference between regarding the embryo as already endowed with an immortal soul or only a tissue or living entity on the way to becoming a human person, remained firm in his condemnation of abortion whether before or after the moment of animation.[2]

The seventh-century Penitential of Theodore decreed that a woman having an abortion after the fortieth day from conception should do penance as for the more serious act of murder.[3]

In 1588, Sixtus V decreed that all penalties of canon law and secular law be applied to all those committing abortion whatever the age of the foetus, absolution from excommunication being reserved for the Holy See. Since the bull met with strong opposition from moralists and theologians, Gregory XIV reverted to earlier laws and the abortion of a foetus as yet 'unensouled' or 'unanimated' was no longer to fall under the sanctions.[4]

In the Anglican Church in 1965 a report on the subject of abortion was prepared for the Assembly of the Church of England and was welcomed by that body, though without an official statement.[5] The report pointed out that the Roman Catholic Church had not always regarded the killing of a foetus before animation as murder. While agreeing that abortion was, in the mainstream Christian tradition, undesirable, the Assembly rejected the moral absolute that from the moment of conception onwards a fertilised ovum had the rights of a human person.[6]

In January 1988 in a debate in the House of Lords, Dr John Habgood, Archbishop of York, stated that in his opinion

> uncertainty (regarding status) is not resolved until the cells, instead of just going through the process of multiplying as happens in the very early stages, begin differentiating . . .

I have not heard of any widespread dissention from this view from within the Church of England.

In 1966 the Social and Moral Welfare Report to the General Assembly of the Church of Scotland took the view that while it regarded abortion as a serious matter, the paramount concern in the Reformed Churches had traditionally been for the mother.[7]

There is thus in the Christian Churches a divergence of view on the fundamental significance of the time of conception, and the status therefrom of the human embryo. The Anglican and Reformed Churches accept the possibility of a higher right and greater good and suggest that the intention of the moral tradition which all Christian Churches share is primarily to uphold the value of human life. They consider that this intention could be actually frustrated by its narrow application in certain circumstances.

One justification which has been mentioned in support of the instant formation of a human being at the moment of fertilisation is that afterwards nothing particularly dramatic happens. The author of such a comment can never have been present at the birth of a live child. Once a baby has breathed, colour and vigour flood the limp form in one's hands. The eyes open, the response of baby to mother and mother to baby is established in an entirely new way and signs of individuality and personality are quickly manifest. In many years I have never got over the drama and wonder of it all. It is of historical interest that in some hunter-gatherer societies who had to limit the numbers of their young for survival, the elder of the family would gently place his fingers in the nostrils of a newly-born baby and it was considered that such a child had never been. It is of interest that in so many languages, including Latin and English, the words used for breath, life and spirit are interchangeable. 'Inspiration' may equally signify the first breath of a new-born baby or the birth of an idea in the mind.

Roman Catholic moral teaching traditionally relies on reason as well as authority and it is to some extent reasonable to claim that the back-dating of personhood from 'the time of animation' to the moment of conception is supported by contemporary biological and genetic studies. It has been demonstrated for instance that all the physical characteristics of a person are genetically determined at this moment. These include not only sex and other physical properties such as stature and eye colour, but it seems likely that general personality tendencies are also determined in this way. Studies on identical twins who have been separately adopted and reared in different environments show that in adult life they resemble each other more closely in temperament, basic intelligence and even artistic ability than siblings raised in the same family. A statistical resemblance has been reported even in their voting patterns and attitudes to such matters as capital punishment, while more and more evidence is accumulating that disease tendencies in later life are also largely genetically determined. There is some truth in the rhyme:–

> There was a young fellow said damn,
> I've suddenly seen that I am,
> A being who moves
> In predestinate grooves,
> I'm not even a bus, I'm a tram.

Doubt may be cast on the belief that a human 'person' is instantly formed at conception by pointing out that a fertilised ovum may go on to develop into identical twins: this can, however, be countered by considering that this phenomenon too is possibly genetically determined and that from the beginning two persons have been present, so to speak, in the mind of God. The remerging of a twinned zygote into one has been observed in the laboratory in some species though it has not to my knowledge been recorded in the human.

There can be no doubt, biologically, that from the moment of conception we have a potential human being fully equipped in the genetic sense, to develop into a unique human person. Before we say that this is an actual rather than potential human person, however, let us consider, say, the fourteen day old embryo *in vivo*. The microscopic appearance is that of a cluster of cells which, although they contain all the genetic programming necessary to develop into a human being, are as yet undifferentiated. In an average twenty-eight day cycle with ovulation at mid-point it is at this stage that possibly more than half are lost in the ensuing menstrual period. These will include the ones which have failed to develop together with those which have failed to implant in the endometrial lining of the uterus. The survivors go on at fifteen to sixteen days to show the beginnings of differentiation in that those cells which will form the embryo begin to separate off from those which will form the placenta.

Many hazards still lie ahead, however, before it can be said that biological stability and secure conditions for development have been established. For example: spontaneous recurrent abortion is a major cause of infertility occurring most often between the 4th and 10th week of development (i.e. the 6th and 12th weeks of pregnancy); some implant in the uterine tube where development beyond 8–12 weeks is virtually impossible and a much more likely outcome is rupture of the tube with death of the embryo and internal haemorrhage in the mother; some will go on to develop an abnormality so gross as to be wholly incompatible with life after birth if not aborted spontaneously earlier in pregnancy; occasionally the cells which will form the placenta develop in such an uncontrolled manner that the embryonic cells fail to develop and a highly malignant tumour results (Hydatidiform Mole).

When one considers such uncertainties it is hard to ascribe to the embryo from the beginning actual *personhood* although highly emotive terms such as 'newly-conceived human being' or 'destined to be a human being' are used by those who are passionately opposed to abortion or experimentation at any stage. This is eminently understandable as the subject is intrinsically highly emotive.

In one of my own pregnancies I had a threatened abortion at ten weeks. The bleeding settled and the pregnancy continued but had it not we would have gone on hopefully to start another. In that case the child I would have had would not have been the one I did have, a different 'person' one might say in truth, yet in no way could a comparison have been made between the one and the other. Personhood in this sense is something which develops only after the child has developed personality.

In Edward Albee's play *Who's afraid of Virginia Woolf?* the opposite occurs. The son, who literally never was, is a powerful 'person' in the lives of his embattled parents but we know they are playing a game. He is a ghost without flesh and bones.

It is my experience as a doctor that in the event of an early spontaneous abortion *personhood* does not come to mind at all, either mine or the patient's when examining the conceptus which is usually presented to the doctor on a sanitary towel. If confirmation is required the specimen is sent to the laboratory without the need being felt for any special container or label: it is otherwise flushed down the lavatory or burned, and the patient, however distressed by her loss does not seem to find this inappropriate. She mourns a child who might have been but never was. The Church forbids Baptism unless some human form can be discerned, which is surely a highly significant difference between theory and practice.

Without for a moment denying the unique place of Man in the order of creation it is clear, in a post-Darwinian era that we share much of our basic physiology with the rest of nature. Natural Selection has progressed by a process of genetic variability and reproductive super-abundance. All species from simple plants and animals to mammals produce more potential offspring than could possibly survive. If every sparrow's egg produced a sparrow all other species would soon be crowded off the face of the Earth.

If every fertilised human ovum were *uniquely* destined by God to be a person in the full sense of that word, it is hard to comprehend why so many should simply fail to develop beyond the very early blastocyst stage, why another should develop into an anencephalic foetus for which no personal activity can be possible and yet another into a tumour. The latter is rare but anencephaly is among the commoner causes of stillbirth: all, to my mind, are highly significant in that they occur at all. We cannot of course see into the mind of God but neither should we be ready to ascribe to His direct and *particular* will something which appears to have neither point nor reason. In addition it seems curiously materialistic to place so much of the argument for personhood on the mere existence of a genetic structure, whether or not it goes wrong. Surely a person is more than the sum of his parts: the role of DNA in the genetic mechanism is a description not an explanation of God's creation of living things.

The development of a person from the ground material of his molecules may be compared reasonably, I think to the evolution of the species. From the biochemical soup there evolved over the millenia a creature with consciousness and eventually self-consciousness. Teilhard de Chardin saw this self-awareness as the basis of the power of reflective thinking and the pre-condition for the development of Man: a being who 'not only knows but knows that he knows'.[8]

The human race together with fossils in rocks *could* have been created by an all powerful God overnight but few believe this was the way it happened. Does it detract from His image to postulate that the acquisition of individual personhood is a similarly gradual process and that it occurs as the embryo goes on to acquire the physical framework necessary to sustain it, particularly perhaps a central nervous system? It has been suggested tentatively (by Häring[9] and others) that this stage of development might be demonstrated in the foetus by the first sign of brain-cell activity which can be detected by electroencephalogram. This would fit in neatly with the current definition of death – that is if the beginning of personhood could be demonstrated by the first sign of cortical activity and its cessation as the last. One difficulty inherent in this suggestion is that improvement in the technique and sensitivity of electroencephalography might allow the detection of primitive embryonic cortical activity at an increasingly early stage of development. This would make the 'time of animation' dependent on the sophistication of the device used to demonstrate it which is clearly absurd. It would seem to be more reasonable to regard the acquisition of personhood as a continuing process which depends not only on the presence of cortical cells but on the capability to form relationships beyond a purely animal response to stimuli. This stage *might* not be reached until the foetus is capable of independent existence or is at least equipped for such existence. Being bodily present is our way of being present to the world and it is through our bodies that we communicate. Can we be bodily present before we are bodily complete?

> The body is the source of all communication . . . the human body is human because it is the source of human communication.[10]

> It is only by directing itself outwards towards other persons and the world that the human interiority is able to become fully a person.[11]

One thing is clear. All arguments for or against the

legitimacy in certain circumstances of termination of pregnancy, embryo experimentation and new techniques to help the infertile such as *in vitro* fertilisation, depend basically on the status accorded to the embryo. Some of these questions will be considered in succeeding chapters.

VI

Abortion

One thing on which all the Christian Churches seem to agree is that abortion is a serious matter. Roman Catholic apologists are sometimes guilty of bracketing abortion with contraception as though they were in the same ethical category, but although it is true that both are concerned with the wide issue of family limitation it is surely one thing to prevent a pregnancy and entirely another to stop it when it is established. Not only is there a conceptual difference of fundamental importance but it is a difference which most people recognise instantly and instinctively. Many women who will use a contraceptive without a qualm will not even consider abortion if the method fails them.

While many people may regret the easy availability of contraceptives to the young and the unmarried a political move seriously to restrict their availability would be unthinkable in contemporary society. There have been, on the other hand, since 1967 several parliamentary attempts to amend the Abortion Act, all with a considerable amount of support from the public. Mr David Alton's Bill in particular in 1987 attracted a huge amount of attention from the media.

There is in most of us an innate respect for living things and whatever has been argued in the previous chapter about the human status of the embryo there is no doubt that it is alive. It is also unique: unlike the genetic simplicity of less complex organisms such as the peas studied by Mendel in his renowned experimental work, the magnitude of the human genetic pool is so immense that the chance of recurrence of an identical pattern is remote enough to be discounted. We are talking, therefore, about the possible destruction of something that is not only alive but the only one of its kind.

Nature, however, is profligate with human embryos and while it is conceded that interfering with a natural process is a different matter from merely observing it, it has to be said that the whole business of medical science is concerned with interfering with natural processes.

Some of the world population growth in this century has been due to advances in the prevention of diseases such as malaria and smallpox and the conquest of others like tuberculosis. It could be said that the administration of an antibiotic constitutes interference with the natural immune reponse. It is rarely suggested however that treatment should be withheld for this reason, although without doubt doctors are interfering with the very basis of natural selection by keeping alive people who would otherwise die.

Few gynaecologists, however, no matter how liberal their views, embark on an abortion with the same coolness with which they would remove an ovarian cyst, and most dislike carrying it out except for serious cause after the 12th week.

A recognised medical nomenclature and the one which is used here is to use the word *embryo* up to the 12th week, which is the period of basic formation, and thereafter *foetus* until maturity, which is the period of development and growth. The word *abortion* under this terminology at one time applied to the loss of an embryo, and *miscarriage* to the loss of a pre-viable foetus (whether spontaneous or induced). Since termination of pregnancy has become more common and more widely discussed the word 'abortion' has come to carry undertones implying surgical interference: many women and doctors therefore are using the word 'miscarriage' for spontaneous loss at any stage of pregnancy, and 'abortion' for active termination at any stage. Terms like 'inducing premature labour' and 'stillbirth' lie in a grey area after about the 24th week.

Those gynaecologists who are reluctant to terminate after the 12th week usually give the reason that the embryo by that time is established and becoming recognisably human. This accords, interestingly enough, with the Roman Catholic Church's teaching that baptism is appropriate only when some human form can be discerned.

Even those women who fight hardest to keep the law as it

stands in order to give them the choice to make their own decisions do not actually *like* having an abortion. Most women are deeply upset by the procedure even when they have seen their decision as right and well founded.

In 1929 the Infant Life (Preservation) Act attempted to distinguish between criminal and therapeutic abortion by stating that it would not be considered an offence if it was committed in good faith in order to save the life of the mother. In 1939 (Rex *v.* Bourne) the law was extended to cover not only the mother's life but serious threat to her physical and mental health. Mr Bourne had performed an abortion without any attempt at secrecy, on a 15-year-old girl who had become pregnant as a result of rape in particularly ugly circumstances. He was acquitted on the ground that a woman's life depended on both her physical and mental health.

The 1967 Abortion Act, as is well known, extended this concern to other children in the family and to their environment. Also, for the first time, it took into account the condition of the foetus itself which could be legally aborted if there was a substantial risk that it would be seriously handicapped by physical or mental abnormalities.

It is of note that the Act is framed in the negative.[1] It is not worded to legalise, far less recommend, abortion in certain circumstances, but to remove the threat of criminal proceedings against both patient and doctor in such circumstances, and then only if it is agreed after due consultation between two medical practitioners. While this distinction may seem casuistic to some, it could equally be seen as reflecting the real aim of the reformers at the time. It might be worthwhile to consider its provisions against the historical background.

In the generation of medical students to which I belonged it was a requirement that each student should personally conduct 20 home deliveries in the summer recess between the 4th and 5th years of study and produce a certificate to show that this had been done. The time was short and it was popular to go to a Catholic country for this purpose where the birth rate was higher, and home confinement the norm. One point was credited for a delivery and one half for attending a miscarriage. Most of us were surprised to find that a miscarriage was a very common event, usually of a foetus at about 14–16 weeks gestation, recognisably human but fitting into a small pudding-basin. It was usually all over before the student and nurse were called. The instructions were to baptise summarily 'if in doubt' and we were shown how to do it; often the husband and children were present.

The mother had to be visited twice daily thereafter to watch for signs of sepsis which was common but she was admitted to hospital only if this became serious. It was some time before experience both in obstetrics and the ways of the world taught me that spontaneous abortion at this stage in pregnancy is quite rare and that these had been mostly self or otherwise illegally induced by women made desperate by poverty and overcrowding. They had no doubt discovered by bitter and painful experience that in amateur hands attempts to terminate were more likely to be successful at this stage than earlier in pregnancy. Subsequent hospital experience in Britain showed a similar dismal picture of frequent admissions of women with life-threatening sepsis or haemorrhage from the same cause.

There is good reason to believe that the Abortion Act of 1967 was aimed mainly at stopping this practice and ensuring that if a woman, usually married and poor, was intent on ending a pregnancy, it would be done early, without payment, under anaesthesia and in aseptic hospital conditions.

From the beginning there has been a conscience clause for doctors, either on grounds of religion or of allegiance to the Hippocratic Oath. The British Medical Association's *Handbook on Medical Ethics* advises that a doctor can refuse to participate in a termination of pregnancy at any stage and in any capacity but that he has at the same time *a duty to assist the patient* to obtain alternative medical advice or assistance if she so wishes. The doctor's conscience does not absolve him in law from treating a woman when the continuation of her pregnancy is life-threatening.

The Roman Catholic Church stands alone among the mainstream churches in Britain in condemning abortion under all circumstances. It takes its moral stand on the safety first principle, that since what it is proposed to destroy could be a person then the risk must not be taken. The traditional analogy of the deer in the bush is often used in moral teaching: if a man was out to hunt deer and he saw a movement in a bush which was almost certainly a deer but which could just possibly be a man, then he would not shoot. The example is not altogether apt for our purpose because in real life it is more likely to be the difficult matter of weighing the serious claims of a woman who most certainly is a person against those of the embryo or pre-viable or non-viable foetus who only might be. The Magisterium is clear, however, in its direction: all human beings are equal in the sight of God and to kill even a potential human being is against the dictates of Natural Law.

The Anglican and Reformed Churches are not absolute in claiming equal human right for the embryo or even the more mature foetus, and take into account what they regard as the greater rights of the mother. They also agree that severe handicap can justify termination, though there are of course personal differences with regard to what is meant by the word severe.

Doctors and nurses who are totally opposed to abortion in any circumstances are probably wise if they avoid hospital practice in obstetrics and gynaecology. Other branches of hospital medicine are not totally problem free however: an anaesthetist might have qualms about colluding indirectly in a termination or a radiologist about ultra-sound screening if he knows that the fate of the foetus might be determined by his diagnostic skill. It is difficult to know where collusion begins and ends because in the widest sense we are all responsible for acts of an elected parliament and for conducting our lives within the framework of the legal system. Some general practitioners who for religious reasons take an absolutist view on abortion, simply tell their patient they will have nothing to do with it and that they must approach a colleague. This policy is eminently understandable but unsatisfactory for several reasons. First of all doctors have a professional duty to assist their patients to obtain alternative advice, not simply to wash their hands of them. A colleague may be known to be sympathetic to abortion in which case there is a degree of collusion only one step removed from direct referral: additionally it involves asking him to take on the burden of something regarded as intrinsically immoral. If he is known to be unsympathetic the doctor is failing in his professional duty to his patient.

Furthermore, patient-care in general practice is a continuing inter-personal and family matter. In group practice, increasingly the norm in Britain, the question will inevitably arise as to whom the patient will turn with her next medical problem or with an ailing child or for advice about how to prevent a recurrence. It would seem that the only really workable decision for a group practice not to be involved with abortion in any way would have to be a group decision. This is often done in other spheres, such as an agreement between partners not to give repeat prescriptions for tranquillising drugs without seeing the patient.

My own policy was to take the responsibility of referral myself. If, after a full discussion I thought the grounds were trivial I stated in the letter only the relevant medical information and why the patient herself thought the pregnancy should be terminated. She was told that it was a matter to be decided between her and the surgeon who might actually do the operation. (This ultimately applies of course in all hospital referrals, gynaecological and otherwise.) In an area where family planning advice is readily available and known to be so, or, even more significantly in an area with a stable population comparatively free from inner city pressures the situation described was quite rare.

If it was considered on the other hand that under the terms of the Abortion Act the patient did have a legal right to a discussion with a gynaecologist she was referred with an appropriate letter stating the grounds on which this conclusion was based under the terms of the law and the rules of conduct laid down by professional ethical advisory bodies. The final decision of course was in the hands of the surgeon and his hospital colleagues. In some areas the referring doctor is asked to sign, with the gynaecologist, the required legal 'recommendation by two doctors'. I have never done this, partly because it has not been the local custom but also because Catholic doctors tend to be treated sympathetically in this matter by their colleagues.

Where the Roman Catholic Church is not the Church of

State and where its adherents are in a minority it is difficult to justify the imposing of Catholic moral teaching on others, especially those who have well considered moral values of their own. They may well be practising members of another Christian church, Anglicans or Presbyterians, or of another faith.

In both hospital and general medical practice it is customary to acknowledge the wishes of those of different religious groups. Most doctors, in another context, respect the beliefs of Jehovah's Witnesses in the matter of blood transfusion but those of us who are of a different persuasion would not ourselves ask the services of a surgeon who shared such views, or at least we would not expect him to apply them to us.

Catholic doctors too should be wary of judging their professional colleagues. They may not share the strict views of the Roman Catholic Church, but it must certainly not be assumed that they ignore the ethical dimension. Most, in my experience, give such matters deep thought even though they may come to a different conclusion.

Since the Infant Life (Preservation) Act was framed in 1929 and amended ten years later, life-threatening complications in the mother have become much less common. Nephritis and rheumatic heart disease, for example, were both caused by the prevalence of infection with the haemolytic strepto-coccus which has since been conquered by penicillin: another explanation may be that the organism has simply become less virulent. Nevertheless there were some, and I remember a few patients whose pregnancies were legally terminated before the Abortion Law Reform Act of 1967. One was a severe diabetic with renal complications whose only previous pregnancy had caused her diabetes to escape control in spite of careful in-patient monitoring, bringing both her and the baby close to death. She had been advised never to risk another pregnancy and nowadays she would have been offered sterilisation after delivery.

Another was a mature unmarried woman whose discovery of her pregnancy after a single sexual lapse had been followed by a near-successful suicide attempt and who would almost certainly have attempted another if the pregnancy had been allowed to continue.

It was at least a year before anyone came to my surgery as a direct result of the reform in the abortion law and I quote the case in some detail as so many people seem to think of termination of pregnancy as the exclusive concern of young irresponsible unmarried girls.

A man came with an appointment in the evening. I knew him well as a quiet but highly respected member of the community with a large grown-up family who had all done credit to their good upbringing. His youngest child was about 20, and he had several grandchildren.

He was painfully ill at ease and it was several minutes before he could bring himself to say what the problem was. His wife, whom I also knew, was 47 and when she missed a period she had put it down at first to the beginning of the menopause. Her last pregnancy at the age of 39 had ended in an extremely alarming spontaneous abortion at about 10 weeks, requiring emergency blood transfusion and transfer to hospital by the obstetric 'Flying Squad'. Since then they had been 'very careful' in their marital relations, and she had had a repair of prolapse with amputation of the cervix. This operation predisposes to miscarriage should a further pregnancy occur and is rarely done now, most surgeons preferring vaginal hysterectomy. She had soon realised, from previous experience, that she was in fact pregnant and had secretly sent off a urine specimen for testing which had confirmed her fears. She was now at about the 9th week and since her discovery had become alarmingly withdrawn, neither speaking nor leaving the house. She had never wanted to have anything to do with abortion nor considered that the issue would ever touch their lives. It was with the greatest reluctance that her husband finally managed to ask if I thought they might be helped under the terms of the new act. He was deeply, though quite unjustifiably, ashamed that it had happened at all and even more that he should even be thinking of this way out. He brought his wife the following morning and she was referred at once to a gynaecologist for his opinion. He considered that she had strong grounds for termination on account of serious threat to both her physical and mental health. He was also convinced that her chances of carrying the pregnancy to term were in any case negligible and had charitably conveyed this conviction to her and her husband. As a result I do not think that either of them suffered from significant guilt problems. She was sterilised during the same admission.

The Roman Catholic Church, as is well known, allows the removal of an embryo or foetus as a side effect of an operation to remove a diseased organ. The example given is usually that of a cancerous uterus when the object is to save the patient's life by timely hysterectomy and only incidentally to terminate the pregnancy. The principle of Double Effect is applied.

Many thoughtful Christian people, including those of the Church of England and the Reformed Churches, do not see a significant moral difference between this situation and removal of a foetus in other life-threatening conditions such as kidney failure or severe hypertension. They might see the object, as in the first case, to be the saving of maternal life and the sacrifice of the foetus as the only means of achieving it, the principle of Double Effect being equally applicable.

Pregnancy in a cancerous uterus is rare but the condition of ectopic pregnancy is not. The Roman Catholic Church allows removal of the uterine tube together with embryo in such circumstances, viewing it in the same light as the cancerous uterus. This is a less straightforward case, however, for the strict application of the absolute ethic. The uterine tube is a 'diseased organ' only in the sense that it contains an embryo which is distending it. Almost always if left alone it will rupture and cause serious haemorrhage in the mother: the diagnosis is usually made before this catastrophe occurs and the tube plus embryo is removed prophylactically. Cases have been reported, however, of the diagnosis having been missed and of the pregnancy continuing in the abdominal cavity with the placenta attaching itself to internal organs. A live baby has been delivered at term by Caesarean section, after this so-called 'abdominal pregnancy'. It is certainly a rarity but one which we were taught as students to keep in mind and I have seen one case.

An immigrant worker who had had no ante-natal care knew she was pregnant and that her time was about due. She arrived at the local maternity hospital considering that she was in labour. She was a thin woman and on abdominal examination the foetal parts seemed to be unusually well defined as though they were just under the skin. Sometimes highly multiparous women have a very thin uterine wall and this seemed to be the likeliest explanation, but she told me it was in fact only her second pregnancy. The foetal heart was heard very clearly: there was a great deal of foetal movement and the head was still high above the pelvic brim. She was very vague about the history of the early months of her pregnancy but had never had pain severe enough to consult a doctor. I referred her to a major obstetric hospital where she was delivered abdominally of a full-term healthy baby which had developed outside the uterus. The placenta had attached itself to bowel and bladder and as surgical dissection would have been impossible it was left behind. At her post-natal examination she was perfectly well and the placenta appeared to have been largely absorbed.

I have never personally seen another case, though one was reported recently (September 1988) in the press, but it must occur from time to time in less developed countries where ante-natal care is sketchy and medical attention in the early months of pregnancy is not always available or even sought.

Could there be a moral case, therefore, for leaving an ectopic pregnancy alone on the slight chance that it might be that very occasional one which survives? If the 8-week embryo really has the same rights as the mother the answer would surely have to be yes. It would certainly develop at grave risk to maternal safety, but so does the one whose mother is in renal failure.

Once again it would seem that attempts to apply absolute rules to particular cases lead not only to impossible medical dilemmas but to philosophical muddles.

FOETAL SCREENING FOR NEURAL LESIONS
In ante-natal care it is routine practice to measure the level of alpha-feto-protein in the maternal blood at the 17th week. Blood can be taken at 16 weeks but is less reliable and a doubtful report would have to be repeated. This blood level reflects the level in the amniotic fluid surrounding the foetus and a high reading suggests the presence either of twins or of incomplete closure of the neural tube which encloses the spinal cord, loosely termed spina bifida. Further serial readings will indicate whether the defect is tending to close or to remain open.

Ultra-sound screening, if it has not already been done, will distinguish twins from a neural tube defect and demonstrate anencephaly which is spina bifida in its severest form. In anencephaly the parietal skull and most of the cortex is absent: only the lower brain which controls bodily functions is present. On delivery a few gasping breaths may be taken but the condition is incompatible with life. Such an incomplete foetus may be regarded as discarded biological material and provided the mother has given consent, be used as a valuable tissue source for teaching or research purposes. Anencephaly, together with the less severe neural defects has a genetic element. A woman who has had one affected child has an increased risk of having another, the chance of a second being of the order of 1 in 20 and of a third (having had two) of 1 in 8.

A higher risk of complications of pregnancy is associated with congenital foetal abnormalities, particularly hydramnios, antepartum haemorrhage and pre-eclamptic toxaemia. In anencephaly, therefore, the woman is carrying at increased risk to herself a baby who will not survive parturition.

The Roman Catholic Instruction of 1987 under the heading *Is Prenatal Diagnosis Morally Licit?* condemns termination in all circumstances: X-rays are vaguely mentioned, a term which presumably refers to ultra-sound screening.[2]

In the case of anencephaly, to induce premature labour to terminate the pregnancy is analogous to turning off the life-support system in a 'brain-dead' person, the system in this case being the maternal placental circulation. There must be few doctors who would hesitate to initiate this, knowing that the mother bears not only an increased physical risk but the psychological agony of carrying a child who will not survive birth.

The following patient was particularly unfortunate.

A woman after a normal pregnancy without hydramnios or any other warning sign, was delivered at term of a baby with gross spina bifida, the whole length of the spinal cord being exposed. It breathed only intermittently and was placed in a cot where it died after about half-an-hour. About two years later, before screening techniques were available, she had a second pregnancy. This time she developed hydramnios at about the 30th week and as X-ray showed an anencaphalic foetus, premature labour was induced. A few years later screening became available for such high risk cases: this involved amniocentesis at about the 16th week. With the promise that this would be done she felt she could risk another pregnancy and this time happily had a normal baby. She decided not to risk having any more and was sterilised.

Nowadays corroborative amniocentesis is necessary only if the level of alpha-feto-protein is raised in the maternal blood. Anencephaly can be diagnosed by ultra-sound as early as 13 to 14 weeks: by 16 to 18 weeks with improved technique less gross spinal neural lesions can be diagnosed which are not necessarily incompatible with life. Accurate surgical and neurological assessment, however, is impossible until after birth. It can also diagnose microcephaly which is compatible with life but is associated with very severe mental handicap. Non-neural abnormalities such as congenital absence of both kidneys and the grosser cardio-pulmonary defects can also be picked up by ultra-sound screening in expert hands: these are compatible with life only if immediate transplant surgery is available; this possibility is remote and most people would doubt even its desirability. The reaction of many viewers to the nightly pictures on the television of a tiny baby who survived ten days after heart transplant was that she might well have been better left to die in peace.

In the case of a baby which will inevitably be stillborn there seems to my mind to be little in the way of a moral problem for either doctor or patient in cutting short the pregnancy. For those conditions which are not mortal but very seriously life-threatening both parents and obstetricians are faced with a very difficult decision about what action, if any, should be taken. Some patients, by no means all of them Catholic, prefer to avoid the possibility of such an agonising dilemma and simply reject the initial blood test, preferring the state of unknowing.

It is a known fact, however, that congenital abnormality and prematurity (often associated) are now the main cause of neo-natal mortality and the benefits of this screening programme are widely accepted by most of the medical profession and by the public at large.

Unfortunately – even with perfect patient compliance (no missed or forgotten appointments), perfect and speedy communication between laboratory and family doctor and instant admission to a specialist unit for amniocentesis – it is very difficult before 18–20 weeks to assemble the information, discuss the findings with the patient and allow her time to consider them before deciding what action, if any, shall be taken.

PRE-NATAL SCREENING BY AMNIOCENTESIS

Amniocentesis consists of passing a fine needle through the mother's abdominal and uterine wall into the amniotic cavity surrounding the foetus in order to remove a few millilitres of fluid for laboratory examination. It is technically difficult before 15–16 weeks to obtain adequate amounts of fluid for testing. Bio-chemical estimate of alpha-feto-protein has been discussed above when it is used to corroborate raised maternal blood levels. Other bio-chemical tests can reveal the onset of Rhesus problems and some rare diseases of defective metabolism. The detection of the latter, however, may require laboratory incubation for six weeks or more, by which time the foetus might be viable. Additionally, cells are shed from the foetal and placental tissues into the amniotic fluid and these can be examined for chromosomal abnormalities with a laboratory result after 10–20 days. Amniocentesis is fairly simple but not entirely without problems: slight bleeding might occur which while in itself not serious would invalidate laboratory findings by contamination of the specimen. In a small but significant number of cases (0·5–1 per cent) it can precipitate a miscarriage. A practical problem is that while obtaining the specimen may take only a few minutes the laboratory examination is highly time-consuming and available only in specialised centres.

For these reasons amniocentesis is not regarded as a routine screening measure: the results would not justify the risk or the extravagant use of laboratory time and manpower. It is reserved, therefore, for those cases where there is a heightened risk of abnormality, the best known of these being Down's Syndrome, which is commoner in babies born to women in the older age group. This condition as is well known can occur out of the blue, so to speak, in a woman who has previously had normal children. There is a demonstrable chromosomal abnormality but it is not clear why this should manifest itself more commonly in the children of older women.

If a young woman gives birth to a child with Down's Syndrome it is customary to examine her body cells for chromosomal abnormality. These cells can be obtained from a blood sample or from a smear taken from the inner side of the lip – a 'buccal smear'. If she is found to be a genetic carrier the chance of a further affected child is 1 in 2. Such women and those over the age of 35 are offered amniocentesis. It should be noted that while all Down's children share a similar chromosomal abnormality some can be more severely handicapped than others. An IQ as high as 98 has been reported: others will have a severe mental handicap and some will have additional somatic abnormalities such as a congenital heart lesion.

Whether or not Down's Syndrome constitutes grounds for termination is regarded by most gynaecologists as a matter for the woman herself to decide. Most of them would offer termination if the patient so wished it, on the grounds, under the 1967 Abortion Act, of serious mental handicap. My advice to those many women who would find such a decision impossible is to decline the test. This is often done and most have already decided on this for themselves earlier in pregnancy, as the following case illustrates.

A woman was rather dismayed to find herself pregnant at the age of 44, but had not even considered abortion. She had four teenage children, one of whom was severely mentally handicapped. This child lived at home but attended a Day Centre for severely subnormal children. The other three were healthy.

The mother felt able to cope with the new baby but fervently hoped it would be 'all right'. They were not a Catholic family. Although she was eligible she declined amniocentesis for screening for Down's Syndrome.

At about 26 weeks she developed slight hydramnios and was referred to an obstetrician who agreed on this finding. Over the next two weeks the amount of fluid increased markedly and she was admitted to hospital for amniocentesis to relieve pressure.

Alpha-feto-proteins were normal and it was several weeks before chromosomal analysis came through by which time she was 31 weeks pregnant. There was a chromosomal abnormality of Trisomy 18 pattern sometimes known as Edward's Syndrome. This is associated with multiple gross abnormalities and is virtually inconsistent with life beyond immediate infancy, if the baby survives birth at all. In this case ultra-sound demonstrated a gross cardiac abnormality and underdeveloped lungs which are common in such infants and the patient was offered and accepted termination on the certain prediction of a stillbirth or immediate neo-natal death. It was in fact a stillbirth and post-mortem examination showed, as well as other multiple somatic abnormalities of kidneys, bladder, digestive tract and limbs the cerebral malformation and cortical cell abnormalities which are the essential feature of this syndrome, and which render meaningful life impossible.

Foetal sex is, incidentally, demonstrated at the same time by chromosomal examination but the only medical indication for specific sex determination would be the presence in the family history of severe sex-linked congenital disease such as some of the muscular dystrophies.

No doubt the number of serious chromosomally recognisable conditions such as Edward's Syndrome will increase with advances in the field of genetics: it must be said that it is both unfair and unfounded to regard professional research workers in this field as being even marginally concerned with breeding a super race or 'ideal person'. This is the realm of science fiction, not medicine. The diagnosis and termination of pregnancy for such relatively minor conditions as club foot and cleft lip are frequently mentioned by anti-abortion campaigners, but have no basis in medical practice. Termination on grounds of sex alone will be considered later.

SCREENING AND THE DAVID ALTON BILL

In 1987 the run up to David Alton's Private Member's Bill to reduce the upper time limit for abortion to 18 weeks demonstrated vividly the difficulty of framing legislation for an issue as highly emotive as abortion. In the media and in Parliament the protagonists tended to present their cases as sincerely held but irreconcilable convictions and the politicians, in so far as they contributed at all, tended to split along party lines.

The present legal maximum of 28 weeks is not in fact contained in the Abortion Act but is a remnant of The Infant Life (Preservation) Act of 1929. The Alton Bill might well have had a much greater chance of acceptance had it not been so specific. Eighteen weeks was an unfortunate choice from the screening point of view for reasons given above and failed therefore to win the support of the medical profession at large, and of important interested bodies like the Royal College of Obstetricians and Gynaecologists.

It can be argued furthermore, that a foetus of 18 weeks looks and behaves much as it does at 17 or 19 weeks. No particularly dramatic development takes place at this point: the organs are complete long before this date but it is not until nearer 24 weeks that the lungs are able to function usefully. Even at this stage there is lack of a tension-lowering substance (surfactant) in the alveolar air spaces which is necessary for inflation and oxygen exchange. Although survivals at this degree of prematurity are recorded they are very exceptional even in a highly sophisticated premature unit and it was for this reason that the judge in a much publicised court case (C v. S) in 1987 found that a foetus of less than 24 weeks was incapable of being born alive.[3]

The legal definition of a live birth is now tending to be directed to function of the lungs rather than of the heart and other visceral organs.[4] It should be noted that the term 'premature' relates to actual body weight at birth rather than to the gestational age which is never more than an approximate estimate. Neo-natal physicians have been publicly criticised in the last few years for deciding to make no attempt to resuscitate certain grossly premature infants. It would be very regrettable if various pro-life groups, however well intentioned, were to force neo-natal physicians to act more from fear of litigation rather than from sound clinical judgement. This seems to be the case all too often in the United States where paediatricians in particular can scarcely afford their insurance premiums. There was considerable relief in the profession when a Glasgow Sheriff Court in 1988 upheld the decision of a doctor not to put a grossly premature baby on a ventilator.

A proposed limit of 12 weeks would have made more sense from the embryological point of view and might have received more enthusiastic support from those who were reluctant to lend their weight to anything less than a complete ban on abortion. 'After a viable age' would have been likely to command the support of the medical profession and the Royal Colleges and would have prevented at least the scandal of termination at a stage when other babies may be receiving intensive care in a premature unit. This is deeply repugnant to the medical and nursing profession as well as to the general public.

CHORIONIC VILLUS SAMPLING

During the months before the debate on the Alton Bill there was a great deal of discussion on the media of chorionic villus sampling (CVS) for the detection of chromosomal abnormalities.

This is a fairly new technique whereby a tiny sample of placental tissue is obtained by passing a fine hollow probe into the uterine cavity. Since the cells obtained by this means arise from the same fertilised ovum as the embryo they have the same chromosomal pattern. It can be performed by those expert in the technique at between 8 to 10 weeks and has obvious advantages for that reason over amniocentesis performed later. The advantages for the patient are both physical and psychological. If the result indicates an abnormality sufficient, to her mind, to justify termination it can be done at a much earlier stage with greater technical ease, reducing both the physical and mental trauma. From the point of view of the surgeon he would be performing the operation at the embryonic stage (i.e. before 12 weeks) which is greatly preferred to later terminations.

Those supporters of the Alton Bill who maintained that this new procedure precluded the need for later and more established screening programmes were, however, simply mistaken. While neural defects undoubtedly have a genetic component this has not to date been demonstrated chromosomally. The condition, therefore, cannot be detected until the foetus has passed that stage of development when the neural groove has normally closed.

Only chromosomal abnormalities can be detected by CVS and while the number of congenital abnormalities recognisable by this means will no doubt increase, they are as yet comparatively few. The technique is more difficult than amniocentesis and laboratory interpretation is time-consuming, not yet infallible and highly specialised. The danger of causing accidental abortion is considerable, much higher than with amniocentesis. For these reasons it is offered only to those women who have a high risk of producing a child with serious genetic handicap. This might include a woman who has had a previous Down's baby and who herself has been shown to carry the abnormal gene. Her risk of a second affected child is 1 in 2 and might be considered to outweigh the risk of the procedure itself. It would not be justified as part of a screening programme for an older but otherwise normal woman with previous healthy children. In areas where it is available the test is confined to those with a family history of severe chromosomally recognisable genetic disease or where serious hereditary disorders are sex-linked as mentioned above.

Termination of pregnancy on grounds of sex alone has caused much recent scandal in the press. Horrifying as it may sound a case *can* be argued that as much psychological damage is inflicted on a Moslem woman by the repeated bearing of female children as on others who have their pregnancies terminated because of different threats to their psychological health. Such women may face divorce and family ostracism and have been known to suffer from suicidal despair. The opinion of one gynaecologist deeply involved in professional ethics (personal communication) was that termination in such a case might be considered to be ethically acceptable only if very stringent conditions were met: that the marital and family pressures were sufficiently severe, that the woman had at least two previous daughters, that she accepted diagnosis by CVS not the later and technically easier amniocentesis and that she understood and accepted the considerable risk of accidental abortion inherent in CVS. She must also understand that such an accidental abortion, if the conceptus proved to be male, might represent her only chance of having had a male child.

POST-COITAL CONTRACEPTION

'Interceptive' methods of contraception which prevent implantation are being considered in this chapter as they effect their purpose after the ovum has been exposed to the possibility of fertilisation and could therefore be considered as abortifacient. They include the interuterine device, some contraceptive pills, the 'morning after' pill and menstrual extraction, whether performed by the administration of hormones or by mechanical suction. (The first two have been considered in Chapter III.)

Menstrual extraction is performed or a drug to induce bleeding is administered as soon as a period has been missed or in the expectation of a missed period before a definitive diagnosis of pregnancy can be made if indeed it has occurred at all. This would seem to many people to be a preferred alternative to possible formal termination several weeks later in the case of rape or abuse of a sexually mature child. The legal position is unclear as it is not covered by the terms of the Abortion Act, but if it is carried out before implantation has had time to occur it may be 'illogical to suggest that there can be miscarriage in the absence of true carriage'.[5]

The Magisterium of the Roman Catholic Church condemns menstrual extraction or induction of bleeding by hormones even in the case of rape or child molestation on the ground that the fertilised ovum has the intrinsic right to implant. Many, both within and outside the Church will find this position difficult to accept.

The Church does not pretend, of course, that a pregnancy resulting from such an occurrence does not present an acute problem to the person concerned and to society. It would urge us to rise here as in all other cases of contemplated abortion to heights of compassion and self-sacrifice worthy of human beings, using all the material and spiritual resources which are available to us.

The intrinsic value of such a general view is not lightly ignored. Christianity can involve the Cross: but we are left with the question of compassion to whom? To a not yet implanted zygote or to the victim of rape or child abuse? Could a child, especially, be asked to make or even understand this kind of self sacrifice?

The well-worn saying that every case is different is platitudinous, but none the less true. In the field of abortion we are required each time to make the notoriously difficult decision about who has the greater claim to be our neighbour.

Infertility

Since the birth of the first test-tube baby astounded the world in 1978 amazing advances have been made in the field of human infertility. The rapid and indeed, alarming, pace of development led in 1982 to the establishment of a Departmental Committee of Enquiry into Human Fertilisation and Embryology which was chaired by Dame Mary Warnock and which reported in 1984.

It is proposed here to consider the various techniques which have been developed in two main groups: first those two which are directed to the production of a child who would be the true genetic offspring of both its parents, namely artificial insemination by the husband (AIH) and *in vitro* fertilisation (IVF); and, second, those which require not only technical assistance but the introduction of a third person into the marriage, namely artificial insemination by a donor (AID) and surrogate motherhood (SM).

Embryo transfer, egg donation and 'womb leasing' are still largely experimental and will be considered briefly later.

AIH was the first of the group to be tried and was condemned by Pope Pius XII on two counts: it separated procreation from the marital act and the obtaining of sperm by masturbation was in itself intrinsically immoral. This view was not shared by the Anglican Church which in 1948 considered that while it rejected AID it did not apply the same Natural Law objections to AIH.[1]

In the Roman Catholic submissions to the Warnock Committee in 1983, several Catholic bodies, including the Guild of Catholic Doctors, were prepared in general to accept AIH. They also agreed with the Anglican Commission that masturbation with the object of obtaining semen for fertilisation purposes was totally different from that 'directed to procuring solitary and self-centred pleasure', and recommended that a different word should be used.[2]

In 1987, however, in its *Instruction in Respect of Human Life in its Origin and the Dignity of Procreation* the Magisterium of the Roman Catholic Church condemned all the new techniques for the treatment of infertility.[3] No attempt was made to differentiate between those methods which led to a genetically true child of its parents from those which did not. A child born of AIH or IVF has a father who is the real father, a mother who is the real mother, it has parents who have a normal continuing marital relationship and it is born after a normal pregnancy and delivery. In AID and SM on the other hand the child is the true offspring of only one of its parents and therein lies, one would have thought, the crucial difference and the nub of the moral, legal, social and psychological problems which follow.

The central moral objection seized upon by the Sacred Congregation for the Doctrine of the Faith leading it to condemn out of hand even the so-called 'simple case' of IVF appears to be the exact *locus* of fertilisation, a point I find difficult to grasp. Also its banning of 'masturbation' to obtain sperm precludes not only AIH but the very diagnosis and investigation of male infertility. The suggestion was made that the Church might allow the collection of semen from a condom supplied with small perforations which would circumvent the accusation of contraceptive intent. Inanimate objects are generally understood to be morally neutral: a bread knife is not a weapon unless it is used to kill somebody. Can a condom be a contraceptive if it is used to collect semen for subsequent fertilisation? If not, holes are superfluous. Such thinking threatens to invite ridicule upon the Church which is painful to those of us who care about its central doctrines and public image.

ARTIFICIAL INSEMINATION BY THE HUSBAND
About 1 in 10 married couples has a fertility problem and about half of these are due to male infertility. If the woman has a normal menstrual history and the pelvic organs seem to be healthy on clinical examination it is customary to investigate the husband before submitting his wife to more invasive diagnostic tests.

I have had only one Catholic male patient who refused to produce a specimen of semen for examination because of the Church's teaching on masturbation. A post-coital test was done but failed to show any active sperm: the test was inconclusive but there was no medical indication to subject his wife to further investigation and the case had to be closed. Sadly they remained childless.

If there is a total absence of sperm in the semen, attempts at treatment have unfortunately a low success rate. If the count is merely low, AIH is usually given a trial by injecting stored and concentrated semen into the uterus at the time of ovulation.

If a low count is accompanied by low motility of spermatozoa their fertilising potential may be tested *in vitro* using prepared hamster ova. If fertilisation occurs the resultant cell division is stopped at the two cell stage. This 'hamster test' has given rise to stories of Frankenstein dimensions of sinister laboratory experimentation on inter-species fertilisation. It should be clearly understood that no attempt whatsoever is being made at 'cross-breeding'. The only alternative would be to use human ova which in the first place can be obtained only by laparoscopy under anaesthesia and in the second place would provoke the accusation of human embryo experimentation.

Many of us would agree with the Magisterium of the Catholic Church that infertility, however painful, must, like ill health, sometimes be accepted. Medical science does not have the answer to everything. It must be admitted too that the treatment of male infertility is usually disappointing, and the success rate with AIH is low.

What is not in doubt is that a couple who are desperately keen to have a child are very much better off if they can be told that there is no chance, or virtually no chance of pregnancy, than to live from month to month in an agony of alternating hope and disappointment. They can then begin to make an adjustment to their lives or make plans for adoption.

Babies for adoption are scarce and the cut-off point with many adoption societies is usually about 35 years for either of the prospective parents. There is nothing more sad than to see a couple go on hoping for a pregnancy until they find that they are too old for an adoption society to consider them, and for this reason alone it is worth making the diagnosis of male infertility.

IN VITRO FERTILISATION

The achievement of IVF has so caught the public interest and imagination that it is being assumed here that most readers will have some acquaintance with the basic principles.

In about a third of women with infertility the cause of the problem is blockage of the uterine tubes. This results usually from previous pelvic inflammation, or from endometriosis; occasionally it is congenital or it may arise from an ectopic pregnancy which has necessitated surgical removal of the tube. It is sometimes suggested by opponents of IVF that women have blocked tubes more often than not as the result of previous abortion, venereal disease or the use of the IUD, and that if the teaching of the Catholic Church had been adhered to in the first place, the necessity for such difficult and morally dubious manoeuvres would not have arisen. This judgement is both erroneous and unfair. While all three may be responsible for tubal infection it can occur just as often after a spontaneous abortion which has had to be completed by dilatation and curettage, probably more commonly in fact because the whole process takes longer. Infection can follow a normal pregnancy and delivery – 'one child sterility' is a well recognised entity – it can result from appendicitis or any other cause of peritonitis: also tubal infection can occur *de nouveau* in a young woman who has never had sexual relations.

The first of my own patients to be assessed for possible IVF had widespread adhesions from a pelvic appendicitis in her teens. At laparoscopy the ovaries were obscured by such dense and impenetrable adhesions that the case presented insuperable technical difficulties and she was rejected. At least she found out quite early in her marriage that conception was impossible and went on to adopt two children.

If the ovaries and uterus are healthy and functioning normally the problem is the theoretically straightforward one of sperm meeting ovum.

The 'simple case' as originally conceived, involved obtaining, through a laparoscope, a ripe ovum from the surface of the woman's ovary at the time of natural ovulation. It was placed in a dish of nutrient medium together with the husband's sperm: if conditions were favourable, fertilisation occurred and when it reached the 8 to 10 cell stage it was placed in the uterine cavity where it was hoped it would successfully implant. In 1978, after years of work on the technique, Louise Brown was born and the achievement was almost universally acclaimed. It did not seem to offend any particular moral principle and it is widely believed that Pope John-Paul I while Patriarch of Venice expressed his delight for the couple.

The procedure is theoretically simple but the low success rate led to the administering of an ovulatory drug to the woman in the cycle preceding laparoscopy. By this means a number of ova can be produced and collected at one time and by exposing them all to fertilisation the chances of obtaining zygotes for implantation are greatly increased. Of those which appear microscopically to be dividing normally, three or four are arbitrarily selected and placed in the uterus with the hope that one of them will implant. As a result the success rate is increasing to somewhere between 10 and 20 per cent depending largely on the experience and expertise of the operator. Unused embryos may be frozen and stored for use in a further attempt if the first is unsuccessful which is common. This saves precious hospital time and relieves the woman of the need for further surgery.

The fate of those spare embryos has since become central to the conflict about the morality of the whole procedure and was one of the main subjects for consideration by the Warnock Committee of Enquiry. The recommendations of this committee are widely known but it would be of interest here to recall the comments of the various churches.

The Roman Catholic Social Welfare Commissions and Committee on Bio-Ethical Issues in their submissions to Warnock, though by no means unanimous, tended to accept any IVF procedure 'which had the settled intent of transferring each and every embryo to the maternal womb'.[4] This would have serious medical drawbacks however. IVF is time consuming for both medical staff and patient. It is emotionally fraught for the patients and it is expensive: there is a long waiting list for treatment. From the medical point of view it would seem unfair not only to the patient but to others waiting for treatment to use anything other than a technique which has the highest chance of success. If ovulatory drugs are not used and only a single ovum is obtained the expectation of success is greatly reduced. A further attempt would mean readmission and another anaesthetic, doubling the time, risk and cost. On the other hand if ovulatory drugs are used and many ova, perhaps 6 to 10 or more are obtained and successfully fertilised it is out of the question, for medical reasons, to implant them all. Multiple pregnancies carry a poor prognosis and while the birth of sextuplets may make a good story in the media for a few days, it is usually a tragedy for the parents. In 1987 sextuplets born prematurely to a childless couple died one by one over the space of ten days, and were a harrowing item on the nightly television news. Multiple implantation of up to ten embryos has been carried out followed by selective reduction (i.e. destruction) at about the 8th week of pregnancy to reduce them to a manageable number. This has been regarded as unethical by the Royal College of Obstetricians and Gynaecologists who consider that it is one thing to leave a fertilised ovum in a dish and another to destroy it once it is implanted and developing normally. As one member of the College put it to me (personal communication): 'How would you like to feel that you had survived at the expense of your brothers and sisters?'

In the Church of England in 1985, the Board of Social Responsibility accepted IVF with the rider that research using spare embryos up to 14 days (as recommended by Warnock) must be directed towards 'worthy causes'.[5]

The Board of the Church of Scotland in the same year was unhappy about any kind of embryo experimentation although it was 'not opposed to IVF as such'.[6] This recommendation carries the inherent flaw that successful IVF, even in the 'simple case', depends on the years of experimentation which have made it possible. It opens wide the question of whether it is ever morally permissible to use information obtained by means which are themselves regarded as immoral.

The Sacred Congregation for the Doctrine of the Faith issued its statement to the Roman Catholic Church in 1987,[7] which to the dismay of some Catholics included condemnation of IVF in all circumstances, even the 'simple case' which most people had expected to be approved. It recalled the Church's traditional opposition to masturbation even as a means of obtaining sperm, but its main objection to IVF was that it separated fertilisation from the specific marital act. It maintained that an ovum had the right to be fertilised within the human body and any other locus of fertilisation offended the dignity of the human creative process.

In its submissions to Warnock on IVF the Catholic Committee on Bio-Ethical Issues had stated that it would not prohibit 'procedures in which sperm and ovum are introduced with or without prior mixing into the womb'.[8] It appears that this might still be allowed under strict conditions, namely that sperm and ovum are introduced separately without prior mixing (lest fertilisation should occur outside the body). Also the sperm must be obtained not by masturbation but from a condom which has been pierced with a hole beforehand.

After normal intercourse the sperm is viable for at least 48 hours and fertilisation can occur up to the end of this period. Chronologically, therefore, it need not be related to a specific marital act. It can take place either in the uterine tube or in the cavity of the uterus: these are hollow organs, the space within them is outside the body in the sense that it is separated from the mesomorphic cells which constitute the body proper by a layer of endothelium. Their cavity is continuous with the outside like all other hollow organs. The anatomical difference between fertilisation in the uterine tube and fertilisation in a dish is that of a few centimetres.[9]

If this argument on the one hand smacks of casuistry, it may on the other suggest that the Magisterium appears to be attaching a great deal of moral weight to a very small point. The object of the exercise after all is to enable a childless couple to fulfil their intense desire to produce a child within the bond of matrimony.

EMBRYO EXPERIMENTATION

The question of embryo experimentation has arisen as a side issue of IVF and together with abortion has generated more heat than any other bio-ethical issue in the last ten years. Occasionally this heat can be due to some misunderstanding of what is involved. It is in fact difficult to keep an embryo growing in a culture medium and it would die within a few weeks at most: furthermore, it is most unlikely that even the most dedicated research worker would wish to proceed further. It is only in horror fiction that babies are actually grown in laboratories: by and large the medical profession does possess some sense of fitness. The Warnock recommendation of a limit of 14 days seems to be acceptable to most research workers and though it appears to have been somewhat arbitrarily selected it does coincide with the point at which the fertilised ovum begins to differentiate. The word 'pre-embryo' for an undifferentiated zygote is being widely, and to my mind, legitimately used. At this stage it is only just visible to the naked eye – about the size of a full stop.

For those who would accord full human right from fertilisation onwards this recommendation and nomenclature will be totally unacceptable. They would point out that the embryo is no less alive and potentially human at 13 days than it is at 15 which is of course true. Three members of the Warnock Committee presented a minority report which opposed all embryo experimentation on the grounds that while there could be no firm decision about when an embryo became a person, it has from conception a special status because of its *potential* for development to a stage at which everyone would accord it the status of a human person. (This argument has been discussed in Chapter V.)

Those who share this view would regard the *in vitro* destruction of an embryo either by allowing it to die or by destroying it at 14 days to be in the same moral category as abortion. The term '*in vitro* abortion', is, in fact, used by some protagonists. The zygote is aborted in the biological sense of having been prevented from developing further but the law pertaining to abortion and the general understanding of it could not be applied. The Infant Life (Preservation) Act refers to procuring a *miscarriage* and the Abortion Law

Reform Act to terminating a *pregnancy*.[10] In the laboratory, as implantation has not taken place, there has been neither carriage nor pregnancy. Almost all would urge that the embryo must be regarded with respect as the ground material or blueprint of a human being even if they would not go so far as to accord to it full human status and rights.

This view includes that of the Ethics Advisory Committee of the Royal College of Obstetricians and Gynaecologists and of the Church of England as expressed in its response to the Warnock Report.[11] Some members of the Church of England General Synod of 1985 pointed to a moral difference between using spare embryos adventitiously available as a by-product of IVF and the direct production of embryos for the purpose of research.[12] Most of those who would allow research within limits are agreed that the cause must be worthy of the material being used and strictly monitored. This consideration occupied a good deal of time in the Warnock Enquiry.

In 1964 the Declaration of Helsinki laid down principles upon which all human experimentaion should be conducted and pointed out a fundamental distinction between research which is conducted for the benefit of the person concerned and that which is without direct diagnostic or therapeutic value to the person subjected to the research. It was added that it was the duty of the doctor to remain the protector of the life and health of that person and that it was essential to obtain valid consent for experiment.

While the principles enshrined in this document are beyond reproach they lead to immediate difficulties in the field of embryo research. The declaration refers to 'person' and the personhood of the pre-embryo is by no means universally recognised. Valid consent is a meaningless term in the same context and the only interpretation of it could be the consent of the parent as in the case of a minor. It is in fact the custom to ask for donor consent, whether from a patient undergoing IVF in relation to possible spare embryos or from a woman undergoing some simple gynaecological procedure such as laparoscopy who might give permission for an ovum to be removed at the same time for research purposes.

To limit embryological research to the strict aim of benefiting the embryo concerned would bring the whole programme to a halt. Successful implantation of the first human embryo conceived *in vitro* followed years of research involving inevitable embryo loss before a successful technique was achieved.

Repeated failure of secure implantation is one of the commonest causes of infertility and a great deal of information on this subject must already have been gained as a spin-off from IVF research. No doubt work will progress in this field as well as in genetics and in male subfertility. The ends can hardly be seen as anything but good and for those who are sincerely doubtful about the means, a very delicate balance of conflicting priorities is set up. A theologian temperamentally opposed to compromising established teaching might see the problem in a very different light from a childless married woman who has suffered the heartbreak of repeated miscarriage: her embryos have already all been lost and she would welcome any research which would give the next one a better chance.

There is a danger that if approval were to be given only to research which would benefit that particular embryo (if such a thing were possible) it would be logical to question the morality of a whole spectrum of medical work involving such well-established procedures as therapeutic trials.

For several years I worked in a surgical research unit attached to a university medical school. The project was related specifically to the problem of resuscitation of severely shocked children. The word 'shocked' in this context means loss of circulating blood volume by haemorrhage, intestinal trauma or extensive burns. As a team we were engaged in serially measuring the blood volume of such children in order to establish a logical fluid replacement programme. There is little doubt that as a result of the work done many children survived who would otherwise have died. Inevitably there were occasions when, in spite of our efforts, a child reached the stage of irreversible deterioration: we continued in such a case to monitor parameters such as blood volume, haemo-concentration and renal function until the moment of death and although it was emotionally harrowing we did not consider that it was immoral. The amount of physical disturbance was kept to a minimum but it could be argued that even that was impermissible. Sometimes a badly-burned child was revived from the initial trauma only to die miserably several weeks later from skin loss and sepsis. This too could produce quite serious and painful self-doubt in those of us who were involved. Since then new techniques in skin grafting and better control of infection have enabled such children to survive and return to normal living, but at the time we had to live with uncertainty and sometimes guilt. Those children would of course have died anyway. They were in our care because catastrophe had struck, which brings us to the proviso made by some contributors to the Church of England submissions to Warnock.

Those who regard limited embryo experimentation as justified for the sake of the general good may restrict their acceptance to embryos which are available as a by-product of IVF. As they have not been produced for the *purpose* of experimentation it can be viewed as an instance of the principle of Double Effect. The Warnock Committee took note of dissent on this point and recorded it in its report.

There is of course, no *material* difference between an embryo which has been produced *in vitro* for the purpose of study and experiment and one which is adventitiously available. Their appearance and behaviour is identical: an outside observer looking down the microscope would not be able to tell one from the other. Each has the same potential to become a human being and both require implantation to fulfil that potential.

I myself can see no middle way of regarding the question. If the potential to become a human person *ipso facto* bars their use, to make a distinction about how they came to be is irrelevant. If, on the other hand, the pre-embryo is regarded basically as a cluster of undifferentiated cells, human, but human tissue rather than human being, their use for study and research for the advancement of medical science becomes permissible.

All cells from the same human being contain nuclei with an identical genetic pattern: this is what makes genetic 'finger-printing' possible in forensic investigation. Apart from the central nervous system, tissue cultures can be made from most body cells but some, such as liver cells, are easier to grow than others. Embryonic cells are particularly valuable for study because of their large nuclei and rapid division: chromosomal activity can be observed from hour to hour.

All medical research must, of course, be subject to basic ethical principles. Suffering may not be caused but if the pre-embryo is only human tissue no direct suffering *can* be caused: the donor has given consent and stands to benefit indirectly.

If these conditions have been satisfied it would seem that the moral question hinges less on whether the pre-embryo had been adventitiously or purposefully available than on the use to which it is going to be put.

In all decision making the intention and orientation of the decision maker is of paramount importance. For the believer it encompasses a sense of awareness of what comes from God. In genuine perplexity when the truth seems unknowable the words of Brother Lawrence come to mind:

> One must carefully differentiate between the actions of the understanding and those of the will: the former are of little value and the latter all. [13]

ARTIFICIAL INSEMINATION BY A DONOR

AID attracts many legal and ethical complexities, but, unlike IVF, it is a simple technique with a high rate of success. For the latter reasons it has been available at infertility clinics in Britain and the United States for at least 40 years. The usual candidate is the fertile wife of an infertile husband, but it may be considered where the man might be known to carry a dominant deleterious gene. The shortage of babies for adoption is almost certainly a factor in increasing the practice; legally it is not regarded as adultery as there has been no sexual contact between the donor and the woman.

For the couple attending an infertility clinic it has the enormous social advantage of being an easily kept secret. Not even the closest of their family and friends need know that their successful pregnancy has come about by AID.

The Warnock recommendation was that at least basic

information of ethnic origin and genetic health should be made available to the child at eighteen, but it is not self-evident to my mind that it is in the child's best interests to be told of its origins. Adoptive parents are invariably advised to tell their child the truth from the beginning and it presents few difficulties. To have been 'chosen' by both mother and father is an easy and acceptable idea even to small children, but many parents would blanche at the thought of explaining AID to a three-year-old even if it were thought to be desirable. If the truth is concealed until the child is old enough and sophisticated enough to understand it, which would probably be the early teens, it could well cause serious psychological trauma at an age when life within the family tends to be experienced as traumatic in any case. In law at the moment there need not be anything on the birth certificate to reveal the child's origins: usually the social father registers the child as his own. To make this more acceptable psychologically and even legally, his semen may, in some clinics be mixed with that of the donor so that he can cling to the slight possibility that the child is indeed genetically his. On the whole the Warnock recommendations seemed rather more concerned with the needs of the infertile couple than with those of the child; most people would concede however that as the practice of AID is widespread, a tightening up of the law as Warnock recommended on such matters as numbers of donations is obviously needed. It has been estimated, for instance, that in a population the size of that of Scotland twenty-five such donations could significantly raise the possibility of later chance incestuous matings.[14]

The Royal College of Obstetricians and Gynaecologists in its guidelines for members recommends that AID should be performed only on a married woman and with the written consent of her husband. Certainly guidelines are necessary because the doctor's role in AID is by no means morally neutral: it would seem that a minimum ethical demand would be that he should have some professional responsibility for ensuring that a child in whose conception he is involved is going to be born into a foreseeably stable family environment. The right to have a child can never be absolute in that it involves interests other than those of the mother, although members of pressure groups for the rights of single women and lesbian couples would not perhaps agree.

The donors are most commonly medical students who are paid a small fee for their services. Warnock recommended that there should be a right to anonymity, although it is obvious that some record must be kept and that it should be clearly understood that the donors should have neither parental rights nor responsibilities. They are screened for genetic defects and a record is kept of race and physical attributes such as stature and colouring.

In the Roman Catholic submissions on AID to Warnock the Social Welfare Commission advised that particular caution must be applied

> where the risks involved something as fundamental to human life as the physical and social arrangements of fertility and as fundamental to the structure of society as the family.[15]

The Church of England response was, after debate, that a majority of their Social Responsibility Board agreed that AID was an acceptable practice for the married. The Board of the Church of Scotland, on the other hand, was not prepared to support 'the unwanted intrusion of a third party into the marriage':[16] this view was based to some extent on a previously published comment relating to the donor that the

> deliberate separation of the responsibilities involved in sex, procreation, and parenting disrupted a set of relationships, physical, psychological and spiritual which together provide a rich soil for human identity and fulfilment.[17]

The Catholic comment seems curiously low-key compared with the severity of the strictures directed against IVF, strictures which would *de facto* prohibit it. Since then of course, the statement of the Congregation for the Doctrine of the Faith in 1984 has condemned AID together with all the other new fertility techniques.

While my sympathy for a childless couple is immense I am not convinced that AID is a desirable solution. The child of adoptive parents is genetically related to neither and has the same relationship to each: the parents can consider themselves equally responsible for him and the way he turns out. The child born of IVF is the child of both parents in every sense. Both children are by definition 'wanted' children whose parents have gone to an unusual amount of trouble to have them, including submitting to professional scrutiny of their marriage. The parents in the case of AID have also very much wanted a child. He is, however, the child of the mother, but not the father, a step-child of the father, in fact, which is an inherently tricky relationship. There must be few natural parents who have not asked themselves at times where one or other of their children got a particularly disagreeable characteristic. This question must be acute and potentially painful in the case of AID: there are difficult times in any family and there must be inevitable conjecture about what manner of man the father was. Even if the child becomes dux of the school the natural family pride of the father may be a little dampened by the thought that the child's inherent brilliance had nothing to do with him, and if all these difficulties are surmountable, there remains the difficult decision of whether, what, how and when to tell the child of its true parentage.

It may be wondered too, what kind of person becomes a donor. The fee is purposefully small so that the incentive cannot be financial; most probably regard it as analogous to the giving of a pint of blood through the Blood Transfusion Service in that the motives are entirely altruistic and the donor has no personal contact or knowledge of the recipient. It could be thought, however, that the donation and acceptance of anonymous sperm to produce a child has a highly charged emotional content which is absent from blood transfusion.

The stance of the Roman Catholic Church on contraception has been questioned elsewhere in this book. A loving and continuing sexual relationship without the necessity of procreation is seen by the writer as acceptable in a way that procreation without the necessity for a relationship is not, more in regard to the donor than to the recipient.

In John Steinbeck's *Burning Bright* the woman contrives a brief and for her distasteful sexual relationship with a

73

younger man in order to give a child to the husband she loves; in the end she is ready to kill her lover for threatening to tell him. This is not being recommended as a solution for the wives of infertile men, but it could be seen as in some ways more human.

There must be, of course, by now, many children born of AID but by the very delicacy which forbids their identification a follow-up study of their subsequent family history is precluded. Without the possibility of reassurance of this nature I would personally be reluctant to suggest AID to a childless couple, however deeply I sympathised with their great desire for a child.

SURROGATE MOTHERHOOD

Surrogate motherhood is not new as can be seen by examining the lineage of many noble families or Genesis 16:1–3.

> Now Sarai, Abram's wife bore him no children. She had an Egyptian maid whose name was Hagar and Sarai said to Abraham: 'Behold, now the Lord has prevented me from having children: go in to my maid Hagar, it may be that I shall have children by her.'

Sarai's 'I' starkly reflects the outlook of patri-linear societies.

Surrogate motherhood is the reverse of AID in that genetically the child is that of his father but not of his social mother. It has attracted much more public attention and reprobation because it is not only done but by its nature is seen to be done. Even with the comparatively modern refinement of artificial insemination a woman cannot easily conceal a pregnancy. Ovum donation would be a more exact biological equivalent but apart from any ethical considerations, which would be comparable to those of AID, it is technically challenging and the indications are few. Among the causes of female infertility, ovarian failure *per se* is comparatively rare. Much more often, apart from the common one of tubal blockage, the cause of infertility in women is associated with implantation and with the inability to carry the pregnancy to term. If a woman's own fertilised ova repeatedly fail to implant it is unlikely that a donated one will do so: if the problem is poor maternal health the pregnancy would be equally difficult.

Two interesting cases have been reported in England in 1987. One was a woman with a healthy uterus whose ovaries had been removed because of cystic disease: she carried successfully to term a pregnancy resulting from IVF in which the ovum had been donated by her sister. In the case of sisters the genetic pool is similar and as the host mother was able to carry the child a normal bonding relationship was established. The donor sister, of course, had to submit to treatment with ovulatory drugs and to laparoscopy, but in the close and loving family relationship which seemed to exist this did not present a problem. The circumstances were unusual, and unlikely to be repeated except on a small scale. The exact obverse would be sperm donation by the brother of an infertile man; it would be simple and it seems more than likely that this has been done but it would not be material for medical or popular reporting.

The other case also involved the sister of an infertile woman. The problem this time was the more common one of healthy ovaries but with the inability to conceive and carry a pregnancy. The ovum of the childless woman was fertilised *in vitro* by her husband's sperm, then implanted in the uterus of her sister who carried it to term, gave birth and returned the baby to its genetic parents. The generosity required of the sister was of a very high order. Not only did she accept the discomfort and hazards of pregnancy and delivery but she faced the emotional hurdle of detaching herself from the newly-born child to give it to its real mother.

A foreign embryo might be thought likely to provoke a rejection response in the manner of a donated kidney, but it could be expected to be less of a problem between sisters: furthermore a baby conceived naturally need not inherit its mother's blood group and tissue type so it may be that there is in nature some natural suppression of the immune reponse during pregnancy. Whatever the technical, moral and legal problems, it seems unlikely that this technique would be considered for more than a tiny number of infertile women.

While Warnock recognised the genetic distinction between

'womb leasing' as just described and surrogate motherhood as it is commonly understood, it was generally biased towards a social rather than biological view of parenthood. This is similar to its evaluation of AID. Its recommendation was, basically, that the act of carrying a foetus from implantation to full term should be regarded as conferring true motherhood on a woman and 'that it was difficult to see any legal circumstances in which this right would be challenged'.

The right has of course, been challenged since Warnock in a long and widely reported legal battle in the United States when the commissioning couple were eventually awarded the right of claim to a baby born of a surrogate mother who had changed her mind about handing over the baby: it is reported that an appeal is in progress.

The likelihood of such conflicting claims with their distasteful publicity and heartbreak for parents and child led Warnock to recommend that to use the services of a carrying mother should be a criminal offence. This was to apply to private agencies arranging such matters whether profit-making or non profit-making. The recommendations were in accord with a statement in the *Journal of Medical Ethics* in 1981 by W. J. Winslade:

> The principle has a potential for economic exploitation, moral confusion, psychological harm to the surrogate mothers, the prospective adoptive parents and the children.[18]

When all the moral, social and legal difficulties of both AID and SM are considered it would seem for many that money and resources might well be put to less dubious use funding an organisation which would tackle such problems as the legal difficulties of adopting an orphan from a Third World Country (though it is accepted that in ideal circumstances a child is better adopted by a family of the same ethnic background). Enthusiasm for research in new reproductive technology has almost certainly been fuelled by the shortage of babies for adoption. It could be said that there is no such thing as an unwanted child. A woman with an unwanted pregnancy would find no shortage of adoptive parents but many childless couples who would eagerly adopt find themselves at the bottom of a waiting list so long that they fear they will be too old to be eligible by the time they reach the top. It may seem to be ironic too that in Britain other children may die while waiting for life-saving treatment in hospitals hampered by understaffing and that research into common causes of childlessness such as recurrent abortion may be limited by dependence on uncertain charitable funding.

VIII

Homosexuality and AIDS

I believe none of the mainstream Christian Churches could find themselves in disagreement with Cardinal Hume in his interview in 1987 on Channel 4 Television's 'Seven Days' when he linked in his mind the disaster of Chernobyl with the AIDS crisis, the first forcing us to consider what we are doing with our human environment, the second our attitude to human relations and sexual behaviour in particular. Nor would they disagree that advocating the use of condoms could be seen as a counsel of despair. None of the Churches condones sexual promiscuity whether heterosexual or homosexual and all would urge self-control and restraint as being most in accord with human dignity and Christian ideals.

The Catholic Church, while fully sharing these views has also a high tradition of realistic recognition of human frailty and a particular emphasis on the doctrine of forgiveness which underlies its very possession of a special Sacrament of Reconciliation. The Gospel which we read with such reverence and emphasis proclaims this truth; no one is beyond the pale.

It is clear that the angst of the widely reported conference of Catholics Bishops in 1986 on the use of the condom as an AIDS protective was based primarily on the thorny question of contraception. Were the protective to be a vaccine or an antibiotic it seems that their concern would be less, or at least different. That the condom is also a contraceptive seems to be the central cause of concern, as they suggested that its use might just possibly be morally acceptable in a case where conception is impossible, for example when the wife is pregnant.

In the homosexual relationship, contraception of course, is not an issue, but the bishops wisely, I think, did not address this question. Is a homosexual relationship made *more* sinful if protection is taken against transmitting a deadly disease?

To consider the normal heterosexual situation and try to apply the bishops' thinking within the framework of normal living: it was their view that if a man has *in any manner* been exposed to the risk of AIDS he may not use a condom to protect his legal wife unless she is already pregnant and conception is impossible. But what if she is using the Safe Period which is not really safe, or lactation, which is only partly safe, or on the Pill or sterilised, which is wholly safe, like pregnancy, but in itself unlawful in the eyes of the Church? The permutations and grades of moral uncertainty are mind-boggling and at the end of the day the ordinary Catholic may wonder what it is all about.

It must be remembered in regard to these strictures that AIDS can be acquired in an entirely unwitting manner. It is well known that haemophiliacs have been at special risk, but it can be acquired unknowingly by blood transfusion or by an infected needle especially in countries where the disease is endemic. Travellers to such countries are now advised to take a small supply of hypodermic needles in case of illness while abroad. The HIV virus can be detected in the blood long before, if ever, symptoms of the disease appear and it would seem to be entirely unreasonable to demand that such a person was forbidden to take steps to protect at least his marriage partner.

Homosexuality is a difficult problem for any doctor and especially for the Catholic doctor when the teaching of the Church is so specific. While the Church may condemn all homosexual practice there is within it, however, a body of pastoral concern for the individual. It is my experience, like that of many other doctors and clergy that when faced with a person with a homosexual problem rather than with the problem of homosexuality, or in considering a couple in an established homosexual relationship, the situation is viewed in an entirely different light. Compassion and sympathy must be especially felt for a Catholic who may be already heavily guilt-ridden, yet feels trapped by his or her sexual bias. It is probable that homosexual tendencies like so many

other tendencies have a genetic basis which may be rein-
forced by psychological factors in the familial and social
environment. Its common association with artistic ability has
often been noted: people who are gifted in the arts tend in the
nature of things to associate with one another professionally
and socially in a circle which by its very nature tends to be
accepting and tolerant. The fact that homosexual relationships arise in this and similar environments should cause little
surprise. Few people, however, would condone homosexual
promiscuity any more than they would condone heterosexual promiscuity.

As a counsellor with a national organisation I have been
involved from time-to-time with clients with homosexual
problems sufficiently severe to bring them to the point of
despair, often from excessive guilt rather than frank homosexual practice as the following cases illustrate.

A man of about 35, successful in business, with a wife and three
children had become obsessed by his inability to pass urine in a
public lavatory. He felt the problem was so ludicrous that he had
great difficulty in referring to it and had never been able to tell it
to anyone, including his wife and his family doctor. It had
reached the point when he was leaving his office at half hourly
intervals to go to the public lavatory merely to see if he could
'manage', and this was causing considerable curiosity and
consternation among his employees. He had stopped going out
in the evening socially in case his male friends should detect and
remark on his difficulty and had been unable to explain this to
his wife, though his unsociability was causing friction between
them. In other respects he maintained he was happily married.
He had been the younger of two boys and his elder brother
whom he described as 'big and macho' had constantly made
disparaging remarks in their youth about his younger brother's
smaller genitalia, suggesting that he was girlish and 'queer'. He
had never had a physical homosexual relationship but was
convinced that his brother's insinuations were justified and that
his apparently successful marriage was a sham.

He gradually came to terms with the reality of the situation
and made a remarkable improvement. The following man
who was older did less well.

A married man in his mid-fifties with a grown up family of three had gone through a difficult patch when the children left home and he and his wife were thrown back on one another's company. They had previously considered themselves to be suitably and happily married. The recent friction had made him severely depressed and had re-opened intense guilt feelings from his youth which he had thought he had buried. He had been brought up as a Catholic and as a boy of about 14 had confessed to his parish priest a feeling of physical attraction to an older boy at school. This had been very badly handled by his confessor who without further enquiry or follow-up had impressed upon him the seriousness and dire consequences of such a mortal sin. From that moment he had secretly labelled himself as homosexual and when his marriage was in transient difficulty 40 years later, took the whole burden of guilt upon himself: 'I should not have married: I should never have had children.' Although he improved and the marriage in time settled down, I do not think he was ever fully persuaded of his innocence.

Homosexuality is one of the commonest sexual variants. Some workers in the field would distinguish between *homosexuality* which would be applied only to cases of established and long-standing physical sexual activity and *homophilia* for cases where the tendencies are confined to friendships of only a mildly erotic nature.[1] Also heterosexual men can display temporary homosexual behaviour in certain restrictive conditions, old-fashioned boys' public schools, prisons and prolonged service in the armed forces being the most obvious examples.

Before the change in the law following the Wolfenden Report (The Sexual Offences Act 1967) which permitted male homosexual practices by two consenting adults in private, frankly homosexual men were subject to ostracism, gossip and sometimes blackmail by the rest of society. A writer of the calibre of E. M. Forster felt unable to publish much of his work in his lifetime. Secondary psychological problems often followed, and suicide was not uncommon.

Homosexual women are less inclined to be promiscuous and often settle down to a happy, more or less permanent relationship. The AIDS problem of course does not arise. There is no legal regulation on the matter of artificial insemination by a donor but the Royal College of Obstetricians and Gynaecologists recommends to its members that it should not be considered, a view generally shared by Warnock.

Society at the moment seems to be going through a period of exaggerated revolt against the stern and judgemental view of homosexuality which was the norm a generation ago. It would not be an overstatement to say that the life of the second man quoted above had been ruined by guilt over something which had been no more than a schoolboy crush on an older boy, a guilt so entrenched that subsequent marriage and fatherhood had been unable to eradicate it. Such crushes in both girls and boys in their teens are so common that they can be regarded as part of normal sexual development. Provided excessive guilt is not implanted most teenagers soon grow out of them especially if they are allowed a prudent and healthy amount of contact with the opposite sex.

Sadly, over reaction to the harsh views of thirty years ago almost certainly underlies the current elevation of male homosexuality to a fashionable cult. The association of drugs, especially, in the United States, of cocaine, and the use of highly-advertised and glamorised 'aphrodisiacs' has given rise to a culture of homosexual excess which is debasing and highly disturbing. The epidemic of AIDS in such an environment and now spreading far beyond it will force us, as Cardinal Hume so rightly stated, to take stock of our human relations and the whole area of sexual education and behaviour.

The epidemic of AIDS may in time cause a reversion to the pre-Wolfenden attitude of the public to homosexual men. Now that the disease is becoming more widespread and can be contracted by heterosexual contact as well as by accidental non-sexually related means this is perhaps unlikely. Along with the fear of AIDS there is a large measure of sympathy for the victims.

The fact that the disease appeared originally (in the West) among homosexual men has given it a stigma greater than that associated with other sexually transmitted diseases; also at the moment it is incurable. Suggestions for a screening programme, therefore, provoke an emotional response and understandable alarm.

A different view might be taken by those involved in medical care and epidemiology, however. For as long as I can remember, pregnant women at their first ante-natal visit have had their blood screened routinely for syphilis and gonorrhoea along with blood group, rhesus factor and the like. Such screening comprises a routine battery of tests fed into a computer. Certainly it never occurred to me speci-fically to tell an ante-natal patient that her blood would be tested for syphilis.

A case can certainly be made for adding AIDS to the list in ante-natal clinics, hospital admissions or any other circum-stances in which routine blood tests are customarily made. Apart from its diagnostic value it seems reasonable to protect obstetric staff and surgical teams. A surgeon uses sharp instruments when operating and birth is an extremely bloody business. AIDS-infected blood could put at risk not only the nursing and medical attendants at the delivery but the porters and domestic staff who handle and dispose of the placenta and soiled linen. Importantly, too, the baby would be known to be at risk and in need of special care. If the test is done I can seen no alternative to informing the patient of a positive result.

To return to the attitude of Church and society to homosexuality the Church of England in Synod Conferences has aroused passionate dissent at times among its members by deliberating openly on the position of homosexual priests when the matter could perhaps more suitably have been left to the discretion of individual bishops. An occasional vicar will scandalise many people by conducting a kind of 'mar-riage' between homosexual men. It might be better if all the Christian Churches could bring themselves to regard the existence of steady established homosexual relationships as a fact of life and a private matter, neither remarking nor condoning but accepting in a spirit of Christian charity.

IX

Death and Dying

For all the current search for an accurate and acceptable definition, the diagnosis of death in ordinary circumstances is not difficult.

A relative nursing a dying patient at home will tell the doctor the exact time to the second that the patient died during the night. On a cremation certificate this time has to be stated and most doctors do not hesitate to rely on such evidence, or on that of a nurse if the patient dies in hospital. It is customary for the doctor to examine the body, and in the case of cremation obligatory, but the placing of the stethoscope on the chest is more a ritual than a necessity. It is common to be called to a road accident and be told by the ambulance driver or policeman that one casualty is badly injured and another is dead. A confirmatory glance is usually enough. In Britain, however, more than half of our population die in hospital or institutions for the old and as a result many people reach middle age without having seen a dead person. The classical death-bed scene with its last words and solemn leave-takings is almost a thing of the past.

In the public mind advances in medicine have almost called into question the inevitability of death and this is understandable when, to take a homely example, a common potentially fatal condition like congestive cardiac failure can be brought so easily under control and the patient restored to many more years of normal living. It is not surprising that people think there is a cure for nearly everything: often doctors and nurses themselves have unreal expectations and have a feeling of defeat and even guilt when medical science fails. To follow the general principle of safeguarding life is, of course, a good general basis for the conduct of medical practice but every doctor will be called upon many times in his professional life to judge when to 'give in' and let nature take its course. This consists almost always of the passive ceasing to strive to keep alive but the circumstances vary so widely that there can surely be no field of decision making more suited to the thoughtful application of situation ethics. A typical example in my experience in the case of the aged would be the following:

An old lady of 96 in a geriatric nursing home was frail and tired both in mind and body and had often expressed her longing for a peaceful death. She developed, quite suddenly, gangrene in the leg: she could have been transferred to a general hospital and had the leg amputated, an operation she would almost certainly have survived with modern anaesthesia: the broncho-pneumonia which would have resulted from immobilisation could have been treated with a battery of anti-biotics. In the event, after consultation with the nursing staff and the relatives it was decided to keep her where she was among people she knew and to control any pain with morphine. She died peacefully after a week.

In the younger patient with advanced malignant or other disease the decision can be more difficult, but the principles of treatment initiated by the hospice movement are being rapidly assimilated into the community and if the provision of specially-trained nurses becomes adequate, dying at home may again become more common.

Sometimes the circumstances can be less straightforward as in the following case:

A 50-year-old patient who was overweight and a heavy smoker, was admitted to a general hospital for an exploratory laparotomy. At operation an advanced bowel tumour was found which had already invaded the liver, and the abdomen was closed without further surgery. Post-operatively she developed a chest infection which is very common after upper abdominal surgery especially in smokers and the obese. For this she was treated with strenuous physiotherapy to promote coughing and expectoration. She found this so distressing that when she was discharged after a few days to convalesce under my care she begged to be left alone. She was an intelligent woman who had guessed, from the evasive answers she had been given in hospital, that she had an inoperable condition. We had always had an excellent relationship and after a calm and honest discussion with her I decided to agree to her request. The family fully agreed and she died, predictably, about two weeks later of broncho-pneumonia, requiring very little in the way of sedation.

It has been said that it is one thing to prolong life and another to prolong dying.[1] Sometimes, in an emergency, life-saving measures have to be instituted in circumstances where the consequences cannot be calculated. The two following examples will illustrate this.

A young man of 22 was severely injured when his car skidded into a ditch on an icy road. On examination at the scene of the accident he was found to be deeply unconscious, breathing only intermittently and very blue: the heart, however, was still beating. He was intubated at the roadside and accompanied to hospital in the ambulance which was fitted with a hand ventilator. He remained in a deep coma for three weeks and then made a complete recovery except for a minor loss of visual field.

If this man had sustained severe permanent brain damage there might have been reason later to regret the resuscitative measures which had been taken in the emergency.

An urgent call was received to a child of 8 who had been found unconscious in a copse of trees with a rope round his neck. He had been playing cowboys with some playmates and it was they who raised the alarm. A passing postman had released the rope. On examination the child looked dead; his lips were blue and his pupils widely dilated but his heart was still beating erratically. Mouth-to-mouth respiration was immediately started but in spite of this procedure, combined with external cardiac massage, the heart beat faltered more and more and eventually stopped.

After about eight minutes both measures were discontinued as it was considered that severe brain damage must by then be irrevocable.

These two cases illustrate the physiological interdependence of the respiratory centre in the brain-stem and the heart which can continue beating independently after brain-stem injury, provided it has an adequate supply of oxygen from the lungs: the respiratory centre itself depends on oxygenated blood being pumped by a functioning heart. In the first case the respiratory centre was damaged in the injury and this initiated a downward spiral by interfering with the respiratory function on which it depended for its own oxygen supply. The heart has its own in-built pacemaker and in a young healthy person it might continue to beat for 10 to 20 minutes in such circumstances until it too runs out of oxygen. Luckily for this young man ventilation could be started before this happened and the brain injury proved later to be recoverable.

In the case of the child, brain-stem injury had been severe from the time of injury (proven subsequently by post-mortem examination). Central nervous system cells are irreplaceable: the quota for each human person and each part of the brain is finite. The presence of a heart beat justified attempts at resuscitation in the emergemcy, but spontaneous respiration never occurred and the heart eventually failed to respond to stimulation. It had been hopeless from the beginning, but impossible to make such a judgement immediately.

In the case of a 'heart-attack' the chain of interdependence of heart-lungs-respiratory centre is broken at a different link. The respiratory centre is itself undamaged until it fails secondarily after a few minutes from oxygen lack. If the heart can be restarted within this time by mechanical or electrical stimulation breathing will usually recommence. If the heart is damaged by a massive infarction it is unlikely to continue to beat spontaneously but often if the damage is less severe death is caused by ventricular arrhythmia which is reversible. Speed is everything in such a case. Such emergencies occur frequently enough both in general hospital practice and every case has to be judged on its merits. A few years ago in a large city hospital a general recommendation was made by the administrators that resuscitative measures were not to be taken in patients over the aged of 65. This caused such a public outcry that it was hastily withdrawn, and rightly so.

General rules in this area of patient care are totally inappropriate as in the following case:

A colleague who is in medical practice in the United States was training for a post-graduate qualification. This involved several years of rotation through different hospitals and hospital departments. While she was working in Haematology she had a severely ill patient with terminal leukaemia, a woman in her late-thirties with a husband and two school-age children. Both the patient and family accepted the inevitability of a fatal outcome and a very good relationship was established between them and the medical staff of the ward. Before the patient died the doctor was moved to Intensive Care and was aghast after a few days to be presented with this patient, now unconscious, who had been tranferred to the unit for intubation and ventilation. In the event the doctor refused to do it and had it not been for the backing of a senior colleague might well have incurred disciplinary censure severe enough to end her medical career.

This case occurred in the United States but similar incidents are widely reported elsewhere. It is true that the term 'extraordinary means' so long used by the Christian Churches no longer includes simple ventilation but the phrase is in any case unsatisfactory as it tends to focus on the type of treatment given rather than on the patient. Intubation and ventilation were indicated and proved to be life-saving in the case of the young man who was severely injured in the road accident but the same procedure would have been totally inappropriate in the case of the terminally-ill woman. They would have been 'extraordinary' in the latter but not in the former. Rules are certainly not the answer although it is true that to advocate judging every case on its merits is to place a heavy burden on the individual doctor. Mistakes are inevitably made and recognised only with hindsight.

Congenital abnormality is a particularly difficult area. Exact neo-natal assessment is not always easy and the mother is emotionally shocked and vulnerable. Sometimes babies born with Down's Syndrome have an associated cardiac anomaly which may be severe as the following case illustrates:

A baby who was the fourth in an otherwise normal family was born with Down's Syndrome: she had a severe cardiac abnormality and required treatment for cardiac failure almost from birth. The lesion was not considered to be operable and in the three years of her life she became more and more frequently ill with associated lung infections. She required constant readmissions to a paediatric hospital and this greatly distressed her. Finally after consultation with the devoted parents the paediatrician decided to treat the next episode of broncho-pneumonia with nursing care only, at home, and in the end she died after a very short illness.

The decision was taken not because she had Down's Syndrome but because her cardiac failure had become intractable.

Babies suffering from uncomplicated Down's Syndrome should be regarded as having the same rights as other children: an intercurrent infection would be treated with the same vigour. There was a widely reported case in 1981 when the parents of a Down's baby refused permission for an operation to relieve intestinal obstruction.[2] The surgeon successfully applied for court wardship and the necessary permission was obtained. The view of both the court and the surgeon was that the child's life after operation would be in no way intolerable but simply be that of any other Down's infant: few doctors would disagree with this conclusion.

I have only limited experience of thalidomide babies. Many, with the aid of modern technology, devoted care and determination have succeeded in living tolerable lives. The following baby was very severely affected:

A child was born without incident in a maternity unit, the last of a large family. The mother had a previous history of nervous breakdown but had been well throughout this pregnancy. Later she remembered that early in pregnancy she had taken, for a few nights only, the remaining few tablets of a night sedative that had been prescribed for her by the psychiatric hospital several years earlier, when the dire effect of thalidomide on the embryo was as yet unknown: thalidomide had been thought indeed to be the perfect sedative with a very low toxicity. The baby was totally without arms or legs but additionally had an extremely small head with tiny eyes. It breathed on delivery but was never vigorous: the mother did not wish to see it and asked, quite reasonably in the circumstances, to be discharged home the following day, to look after her other children. The baby was lovingly nursed by the staff and offered drinks of glucose-water only, for comfort. These were immediately regurgitated and the baby died after two days. It was clear that it had stenosis of the oesophagus as well as all the other abnormalities. Surgical correction of this latter condition is a major undertaking even in an otherwise healthy baby and referral was not contemplated here.

The degree of disability in spina bifida babies varies enormously but without closure of the defect the child will die of infection. Most neuro-surgeons have a grading system for assessing operability. If the findings are truly marginal and the final decision is left to the parents they require a good deal of support whichever way they decide. Those who decide to have nothing done are probably the more vulnerable and are greatly helped if the family doctor strongly reassures them that they have made the right decision whatever his own personal feelings might be. Guilt is very common after such an agonising choice and is easier for the parents to bear if it is shared in this way.

This is equally applicable in the case of the family of a seriously ill aged relative, perhaps with pneumonia following a stroke. The doctor might very obliquely seek the family feeling but if it is clear that their inclination is to let the patient die in peace it is, in my opinion, best that they should be left with the impression that they are agreeing with the doctor rather than the other way round. A devoted daughter may say that she would 'never forgive herself' if she thought she was hastening her aged mother's death and it seems unfair to lay this whole burden on someone who is already emotionally overwrought.

I accept, however, that this personal viewpoint may well be considered to be against a general trend towards encouraging people to make their own decisions and take full responsibility for their actions in all areas of life.

TELLING THE PATIENT

There is a general bias now towards telling the patient the truth, an attitude largely assimilated from the United States. There is no doubt in my mind that this is a better way than evasion and in the case of malignant disease the sooner the patient is told the better. If he has a lump which might be malignant and he is told at the time he and his doctor can tackle the problem together, stage by stage: respect for personhood is basic here. The following case illustrates this point.

A man of 30, married with two children came with a lump in the testicle and a malignant condition was suspected from the first examination. He had hoped for reassurance but the possibility of malignancy had been in his own mind. He was referred for biopsy which confirmed a testicular tumour and he was told of the report immediately. He was also told that while such tumours can be highly malignant they are also very sensitive to radiotherapy and chemotherapy. He required a long course of both and had a very bad time, being miserably nauseated for days at home after each weekly out-patient treatment over about a year. He lost all his hair and became anaemic but bore it all with great fortitude. He was greatly helped by his wife who had been fully in the picture from the beginning and encouraged him when his spirits drooped from time to time. Because he had been told the truth from the very first they knew the treatment was life-saving and there is little doubt that this kept them going. He made a complete recovery and remains well many years later.

Except for a few patients known to be unable to cope with psychological pressure this policy of telling early is the one of choice. Too many patients used to come out of hospital after an operation for an 'ulcer' and were totally unprepared for possible deterioration as in the following case:

A single well-educated professional woman came with symptoms suggesting appendicitis. A mass which was easily felt in the abdomen seemed almost certain to be an appendix abscess. She was sent to hospital and the surgeon agreed, treating her conservatively as an in-patient for ten days, and planning to re-admit her later for appendicectomy. Just before discharge she suddenly developed intestinal obstruction requiring urgent operation: unfortunately the mass was not an appendix abscess but a tumour of the bowel with secondary deposits already in the liver. The obstruction was by-passed and she was, for some reason, not told the truth: most probably the emergency surgeon had not been the one in overall charge of the case. When she came home she was perplexed and frustrated by her slow convalescence and fretted about getting back to work, though she admitted she did not feel up to it. It fell to me to tell her the truth, which, in fact, was a great relief to her. She had always thought herself to be physically and mentally tough as indeed she was, and the true diagnosis now explained her failure to recuperate. She faced further deterioration unflinchingly and a few months later died peacefully.

If the truth is told early enough it can be coupled with hope and encouragement. With few exceptions not to tell patients the truth seems to be robbing them of their very dignity and if it is not done at the beginning it is very difficult to do so later on. Meantime a process of systematic deception is set up between doctor and patient, often involving the closest members of the family. It is very sad, in what has been a good marriage, when one spouse insists on deceiving the other to the very end. The patient, who will probably have his own suspicions, must feel very alone facing the most awesome part of his life: his wife, with whom he had previously discussed everything, is not available at the end. Sometimes a circle of deception is set up when he does not wish to distress her by telling her that he knows and she assumes a false cheerfulness which is painful for them both. The doctor who participates in such a deception loses not only the trust of the patient but of the rest of the family when they have had time to think about it and themselves fall ill.

Even when the outlook is bleak the patient usually benefits from being told the truth. Most of us, probably, fear dying more than death and if the truth has been told, assurance can be given of good care and adequate pain relief when it is needed. While totally avoiding the direct imposition of his religious beliefs upon a patient the doctor who has a religious basis in his own life and work might well ask as he walks up the garden path for his daily visit that God should be that day in his head and in his understanding and in his mouth and in his speaking. If it is appropriate the priest or minister can be involved from the beginning rather than at the end as the herald of death, as has been so often the case in the past. In such circumstances if it can be achieved, a good doctor-clergy relationship can be of immeasurable benefit to all concerned.

THE TREATMENT OF THE AGED

Advances in medical care coupled with a generally rising standard of living have brought about a dramatic increase in the numbers of aged people in the population. About a fifth of all admissions to NHS hospitals is of people over the age of 75; such patients usually have multiple pathology and their hospital stay is therefore more likely to be prolonged. Since the stock of brain cells in each person is finite the number of old people suffering from some degree of confusion will rise concomitantly with increasing life expectancy.

As every doctor knows, once an old person has been in hospital for a prolonged period it is very difficult to resettle them in the community. It can be a major problem to find a suitable placing for an old person who no longer needs hospital care but is not quite fit enough to live alone at home. While it may be considered that children should have an obligation to care for elderly parents it should not be presumed that the old person will not resent feeling obliged to a son or daughter. One of the best investments the health and social services could make would be to fund and encourage simple measures to help old people to stay in their own homes. Illich (1975) argues for a refocusing on the priorities of health care:

> Dependence on professional intervention tends to impoverish the non-medical health-supporting and healing aspects of the social and physical environment.[3]

Local authorities who are forced to economise on their home-help services simply provoke an increased demand for residential accommodation or hospital care which is very much more expensive. Apart from the economic factor most old people prefer to live at home, and it would be reasonable to ask, when a move to residential accommodation is being contemplated, whether it is directed towards the real welfare of the person concerned. It is questionable if even moderate dementia is sufficient ground as long as the old person is reasonably safe and reasonably nourished. Many old people live in contented confusion and dubious hygiene perhaps with a cat or dog. For many years I visited an old lady who, once her few medical problems had been disposed of, was always eager for a cup of tea and a chat. The tea cup was cursorily wiped with the floor cloth she used to clean up after her cat but neither of us ever came to any harm and I always looked forward to her sharp and witty comments on current affairs. She invariably slept with her feet on the pillow and her head at the bottom of the bed for the very good reasons that the first elevated her swollen ankles and the second gave her a view of the birds at the window: she was considered by some people to be quite seriously demented. Although a patient such as this may worry their family, friends and neighbours, moving her to a 'home' however cleaner, warmer and safer, is not necessarily in the old person's best interests. Money is well spent on home helps, 'Meals on Wheels' and day centres where the old person who is just managing at home can go occasionally to have a bath and other necessary bodily attention. The right of such a person to stay at home can be defended on human grounds even if they are conceded to be at some personal risk.

For the doctor, when to treat and not to treat a demented old person can be a difficult problem as the line between mental competence is likely to be indistinct. Intellectual impairment is uneven and an old person who is confused about day-to-day matters may have well-considered opinions about her future. It is a case for individual judgement and often the only thing to do is to try to discern from previous knowledge of the person what he or she would be *likely* to want.

This applies not only to treatment but to medical investigation; if a frail old lady in her nineties becomes anaemic her gastro-intestinal tract would be suspected of bleeding from some part. A barium meal X-ray examination is not too unpleasant but bowel examination certainly is: if anything were to be found such as a cancer of the colon, would she want or could she stand an operation? Hospital diagnostic departments themselves are confusing and frightening to old people. If a tumour were to cause an acute obstruction of course, operation would be indicated at once to relieve distress, but apart from the possibility of this emergency, might it not be better to let her fade away quietly and peacefully from anaemia? The answer must be that sometimes it would and sometimes it wouldn't and one can only hope for the grace to make the right decisions most of the time.

Respect for personhood is the overriding consideration in the treatment of the aged. It is doubtful if it is ever ethically legitimate to remove an old person from his home against his will for the peace of mind of neighbours, social workers or a concerned family. Their criteria of what is best for an aged relative – warmth, safety, hot meals – may not be those of the old person himself: he (or more likely she) might prefer risking a fall in a cold kitchen and dying of hypothermia to the most luxurious eventide home or to moving in with a son or daughter in an unfamiliar area away from friends.

Serious dementia is, of course, a different matter and increasingly common: in-patient care may be the only option. Such people have become mentally handicapped and the relationship of professional carers is very similar to that which exists with other mentally-handicapped adults. Their dignity is of great importance but many decisions have to be taken on their behalf and the questions of when to treat and when to investigate rest even more firmly on the shoulders of the doctor. A demented person may not necessarily be unhappy, and may have an inner life not detectable to the outsider. A terminally-ill person in another age group, such as a younger patient with malignant disease, often has his life legitimately shortened by the adequate administration of powerful pain-relieving drugs. The principle of Double Effect is suitably applied in such a case. Demented old people rarely require such drugs so that a decision to allow to die will usually involve the withholding of specific treatment for intercurrent illness. Decisions concerning which therapeutic means are appropriate is a matter for fine medical and nursing judgement. While too many of the trappings of hospital care are undesirable and distasteful both for the dying person and his family a catheter in the bladder may be much more comfortable and unobtrusive than a wet bed and constant changing: an intravenous saline drip into the back of the hand is discreet and unencumbering and will relieve distressing symptoms of dehydration in a febrile patient. These measures make dying more comfortable without significantly affecting the outcome and detract nothing from the dignity which most of us desire at the end. The compassion and skill of the hospice enables dying people to participate in the management of their own dying. Most of us die in less well ordered circumstances of diseases associated with growing old. Old people too need help actively to disengage from former activities and responsibilities and to prepare for the time when they must let go altogether and say 'into Thy hands'.

EUTHANASIA

This is a subject which generates much heat in general discussion but it has been my experience in real life that the question is rarely encountered.

The word is here being used in its modern and more usual sense of the direct termination of a patient's life at his specific request in the face of an illness he is finding intolerable. Its literal sense of a good or easy death is no more than we would all wish for and which should be offered by good terminal care. Allowing to die by standing back and letting nature take its course has already been discussed and is part of good and well-judged professional care: it is sometimes referred to as 'passive euthanasia', but this seems to be a needlessly confusing term.

Many patients facing terminal illness will ask overtly or circumspectly to be assured that they will be kept as free as possible from distress and pain. When the end is in sight they or their family may make it explicitly clear that they would prefer adequate sedation to a few extra days of dying. In such circumstances the morality of the principle of Double Effect is rarely questioned by either patient or doctor. It is not even customary to enter sedation as a contributory cause of death on the death certificate, though it is certain that this has often been the case. Patients with malignant disease may have been receiving high doses of powerful analgesics by the end. Hospice-type management is spreading rapidly in the community and a woman with cancer of the breast, for example, which has spread to bone may be started and maintained comfortably on oral diamorphine while continuing to play a reasonably active role in family life. Large doses are not necessary at first if correctly administered with the patient's co-operation but they are of course stepped up if the need increases and tolerance possibly develops. Powerful drugs should never be withheld for reasons of medical timidity – the dosage should always be governed by the patient's needs. Correct combinations of analgesic drugs used in conjunction if necessary with specific nerve-blocking techniques can allow a patient to be both reasonably alert and pain free, and confidence that their needs will be met is a very important factor in the maintenance of patients' morale. There is nothing more distressing than to see a patient dying in an acute general hospital which is not appropriate to his needs. He anxiously watches the clock waiting for the statutory four hours to pass before he will be 'due' for another injection. The hospice methods have overcome this problem and deserve high praise.

There is a common and distressing condition frequently met in general practice which is much more difficult to handle. This is emphysema, often the late result of chronic bronchitis, where the actual alveolar lung tissue has been destroyed. It is in the alveolar air spaces that oxygenation of the blood takes place and sufferers are chronically short of breath. In the late stages they use all the accessory muscles of respiration to inflate their remaining lung tissue to the full: they literally have to stay awake to breathe. They are not in pain but simple sedatives to encourage sleep are ineffective for the foregoing reason. Oxygen from a cylinder helps a little, but terminally such patients are in a very pitiable condition. Morphine is the only drug which gives real relief by diminishing the actual body cell requirement for oxygen, but there is no doubt that even in a small dose it will reduce the respiratory drive and directly hasten or precipitate death.

Whether, and if so, when to administer morphine to such a patient calls for considerable medical judgement and even courage. It is probably in treating cases of respiratory distress that most doctors come nearest to practising euthanasia.

Doctors must be clear. To hasten a patient's end *deliberately* even by a few days, is legally regarded as murder. The category of 'mercy killing' does not exist in law, though a court might be expected to reduce a charge to manslaughter: such a charge is in fact rarely heard. Ethically, and therefore most importantly, it would seem that the *intention* of the doctor is the overriding factor. There is a clear moral difference between an actual intention to kill and taking even the admittedly high risk of administering a powerful sedative to a patient in respiratory distress with the primary intention of giving him a night's rest.

With regard to the question of legal euthanasia it is widely reported that the majority of the lay public supports the provision of positive help towards a rapid and peaceful death. If such a procedure were to be legalised the immediate question would arise as to who would carry this out. I know of no survey of medical opinion on the matter but I would expect that most doctors would regard such legislation as an intolerable and indeed unthinkable threat to the trust between patient and physician which is central to medical practice and enshrined in every professional code.

Transplant Surgery

Kidney transplant is now a well-established procedure to which few people have any ethical objection. In the early years, even when related donors were used, the problems of tissue matching and rejection were very great, but many of these difficulties have been overcome and there is now a high expectation of success. The fact that we have two kidneys makes live donation possible and in some centres, notably in Scandinavia, cadaveric transplant is almost a thing of the past. While donating a kidney is hardly analogous to giving a pint of blood the danger to the donor that the other kidney might fail is considerably less than 0.1 per cent. The advantages of live donation are of course enormous. Not only is the kidney absolutely fresh but tissue matching has been carried out at leisure and the operation arranged well in advance so that the recipient, who is probably on dialysis several times a week, is both physically and psychologically prepared. In the case of cadaveric donation the midnight telephone call to alert patient and transplant team places a tremendous strain on both recipient and hospital. Live donation of a kidney to some young relative in renal failure is thus an act of admirable and usually rewarding charity.

A cadaveric kidney must be removed quickly after death if it is to be useful. The word 'donor' is a euphemistic word for a young person who has most likely been killed in an accident. Obtaining consent therefore almost inevitably involves approaching a bereaved family while they are still shocked and distressed. The suggestion has been made that the law should be changed to presume consent unless otherwise stated.[1] People fail to carry organ donation cards more often through inertia than considered opposition and it seems reasonable to expect that many lives could be saved if the law could be changed in this way.

The recent report of success using a pig's kidney may represent a major breakthrough and unless there is an objection to killing animals for any reason whatsoever including food, there seems to me to be no substantial ethical problem. Pigs' heart valves have been used in cardiac surgery for several years and 'catgut' (usually sheep's gut) sutures have been used in routine surgery for decades because of their absorbable quality. Many people who will not eat meat for humanitarian reasons wear leather shoes or play a musical instrument with gut strings. If there is an objection it would have to be a consistent one.

Live donation of single vital organs is, of course, by definition impossible. Cadaveric liver transplant is as yet less successful than that of the kidney but no doubt the many technical and rejection problems may be overcome. Heart transplantation is the procedure which is not only the most dramatic but the one which produces the greatest emotional response. This should cause little surprise since the heart has been perceived for so long in history and in literature as the source and essence of life and personhood. It is true however that

> from the biological point of view a transplanted heart is less apt to injure the spiritual personality of the recipient than are certain currently accepted psychiatric and neurosurgical techniques.[2]

Since the circulatory system works on the ordinary principles of hydrodynamics and the heart is merely the pumping mechanism the same comment would apply to a mechanical or animal heart if such a thing were to become a practical possibility.

The main ethical problem in heart transplantation seems to be in justifying such elaborate procedures to prolong the life of a person whose expectation of life is in any case poor. It is unlikely to be considered unless the recipient's heart is in intractable failure; in such circumstances the secondary effect of cardiac failure on other organs may already be severe and irreversible. The post-operative mortality is high and the most that can be hoped for in most cases is a very few more years of survival. Heart transplant in neo-nates seems to be particularly questionable. Even if it is successful the problem of growth has to be dealt with: will the heart grow with the baby and what will be the effect of immuno-suppressive drugs on the baby's own growth? Because something *can* be done, it does not necessarily mean that it *should* be done. The whole problem lies in the difficult area of balancing the particular against the common good. If the money spent on heart transplantation were to be used to fund a heart-disease prevention programme or to reduce the waiting list for simpler, more successful heart operations (such as coronary by-pass or the correction of some congenital cardiac defects) there is no doubt that the common good would be better served. That kind of problem, however, is encountered by all of us in daily living. The only practicable guide is probably the old wisdom that you must do what you can, but can do only what you *can* do. If I am a doctor I can only devote my skill to the treatment of each individual patient with heart disease: if I am a health minister I will devote my energy to improving the nutritional balance of school meals and discouraging cigarette smoking.

DIAGNOSIS OF DEATH

It has been said earlier that the diagnosis of death is usually easy. The development of sophisticated ventilatory techniques for patients in a coma from brain injury provide circumstances in which this statement does not apply. Body cells die at different rates: the brain cells are least able to withstand anoxia and die first while those of skin, nails and hair follicles may live for one or two days longer. The term 'brain-death' has become popular with the lay public but brain cells too die at different rates: the cortical cells first, then the thalamus and last the brain-stem which includes the respiratory centre. It is thus necessary to make a distinction between human life and biological life. Human life is associated with cortical activity and the viability of cortical cells can be demonstrated by electro-encephalography. A flat response after standard stimulation procedures is usually taken to mean the end of human life and this test repeated and confirmed by more than one doctor is normally taken as an indication for turning off the life-support system. It should be noted that in human terms the patient is dead *before* the machine is switched off, a point which many people fail to grasp and which is the source of much natural anxiety.

If it is planned to use the organs for transplant after cortical death has been established there are several alternatives open to the transplant team after finding and preparing a suitable tissue-matching recipient. If the ventilator is stopped the respiratory centre in the brain stem will quickly die from lack of oxygen supply. The heart is less susceptible to anoxia than the brain and is likely to continue to beat for some minutes until it too runs out of oxygen. After cessation of the heart beat the patient is dead by conventional as well as neurological standards and the required organs are removed as soon as possible for immediate transfer, freezing or perfusion. So that his organs remain in good condition the donor must already have been moved to the vicinity of an operating theatre before the ventilator is stopped. For the sake of the relatives it would seem best that they should be informed that the patient is dead as soon as it has been confirmed and that the time given on the death certificate should relate to this moment.

Since organs begin to deteriorate immediately their blood supply stops the 'beating heart donor' is an alternative and logical source of transplant material although it must be stated that there are transplant surgeons as well as many members of the public who are unable to accept this. The argument for the procedure on purely biological and utilitarian grounds is irrefutable. If the organs are to be donated it is reasonable to ensure that they are in the best possible condition: there can be no more efficient way of achieving this than to maintain the heart and circulation by keeping the donor on the respirator and continuing to ventilate the lungs until the recipient is surgically prepared. The donor has been pronounced cortically and therefore humanly dead and simple ventilation of his lungs is more efficient and effective than any heart-lung machine or perfusion apparatus which could be substituted in an operating theatre: the donor's body *is* in effect a biological heart-lung-perfusion machine.

The arguments against beating-heart donation must there-fore be on a different plane. Some surgeons instinctively recoil from the idea, even although they know the standard tests for death have been applied and the criteria fulfilled. Others who do not, and consider the recipient's needs to be paramount may nevertheless clear the operating theatre of nurses and auxiliary staff to spare their feelings until the donor heart has been removed and his body taken out of the theatre. It has been suggested that a general anaesthetic could be given just in case there was pain, but this is not reassuring. For the relatives of the donor it asks a degree of superhuman scientific detachment which can be by no means assumed in the emotional circumstances of the death of a young person. However well they may have been prepared it may seem humanly inappropriate to deny them a time of quiet leave-taking free from the background noise and impedimenta of the life-support system. It is possible too that the lamentably small number of people who carry organ donation cards would diminish even further if they thought their organs might be taken before they were 'really' dead.

While the recipients would undoubtedly gain, it is an area where utilitarian considerations are of doubtful supremacy and provides yet another example of the difficulty of discerning in any given situation who is one's neighbour.

THE FOETUS AS DONOR

There was considerable disquiet early in 1988 when it was reported that a transplant of brain tissue from a dead foetus had benefited a patient with Parkinson's Disease.

The term 'stillborn' is applied to a baby born after the 28th week of pregnancy which has 'not breathed or shown other signs of life'. It is registered as such and it is customary for the parents to make some arrangement for burial. The stillborn infant is the property of its parents and their permission is required before any of its organs or tissues can be used for donation or experiment. The '28 weeks' is a relic of the Infant Life (Preservation) Act and as babies more premature than this have survived it is clearly no longer appropriate. (The Act does not apply, incidentally, in Scot-land.) It must be remembered, too, that gestational age is never more than an approximation, so that 'breathing and other signs of life' are more important factors than prematurity *per se*. A premature infant born at 26 weeks which succumbed after a week would be considered like any other baby to have 'died'. Pre-viable and incomplete foetuses have been, for practical purposes, regarded as discarded biological material and while the mother would, of course, have the right to refuse permission, they have traditionally been available for research or teaching purposes. Outside teaching hospitals and research centres it is customary to dispose of them by incineration. The Christian Churches, including the Catholic Church do not seem, in practice, to have clear-cut procedures for either baptism or burial in such circumstances and while a mother will grieve over a spontaneous abortion or miscarriage she tends, in my experience, to have neither curiosity nor strong feelings about the physical disposal of the conceptus. There is no doubt that a great deal of study useful to the human race has been and is being carried out on foetal tissue salvaged in this way.

If there is an ethical problem in respect of foetal tissue for transplant it must hinge on the question of whether an abortion has been spontaneous or induced. In either case the conceptus once separated from the mother is dead. The considerations are in some ways similar to those which apply to the 14-day embryo and the legitimacy of experimentation upon it. A moral distinction has been made by some of the Churches between those embryos which are adventitiously available as a by-product of IVF and those which might be produced for the express purpose of experimentation. The embryos are indistinguishable biologically and equally useful: the dead foetus from a spontaneous abortion or miscarriage is similarly indistinguishable from that produced as a result of active termination of pregnancy: both are common, however regrettable that may be. In view of this wide availability it seems to me to be unduly alarmist to suggest that the use of foetal tissue for transplant or research might lead to inducing women to breed and abort foetuses expressly for the purpose, or that a neurosurgeon would actively persuade a gynaecological colleague to terminate a pregnancy in order to provide him with foetal brain tissue.

It is difficult, if not impossible to take a general moral stand on transplant surgery. Each procedure has a different ethical content and while kidney transplant seems virtually free from moral problems it too can be open to abuse: cases have been reported of poor people in Latin America and Turkey selling one of their kidneys to a rich recipient. While the use of the 'beating heart donor' seems instinctively, to me, to be a distasteful procedure there are others who would claim that a desperately ill recipient has an overriding claim. Human organs do not have the status of a human person but the considerations of human dignity and public disquiet should never be brushed aside or disregarded.

The Harm We Do

They are not Gods
though they would like to be;
they are only a human
trying to fix up a human
. . .[1]

The dispensing of both drugs and advice is a tricky procedure and of particular concern perhaps to the family doctor who has the patient in his long-term care and who may enjoy a degree of personal trust and confidence not shared by a hospital department. He has the traditional authority to 'certify' whether or not a patient is fit for work or whether some complaint merits referral for further investigation.

Doctors do know more, in general, than their patients about bodily health and disease so that some of their authority is reasonably derived from this specialised knowledge. I am sometimes surprised at the degree of ignorance of basic human physiology in some intelligent and otherwise well-informed people. To respect a doctor on these grounds would be analogous to respecting an electrician or motor mechanic when the problems arise in another area.

There is a danger, however, which applies also to the priest, that too much paternalistic authority might be encouraged by patients and become a substitute for the more difficult task of ordering their own lives wisely. A balance has to be struck between discouraging this and adopting a false egality which would deny to the doctor or the priest any authority whatsoever and render him professionally ineffective. Even well-informed patients cannot be expected, for instance, to balance the therapeutic usefulness of any drug against its possible side effects.

In the following case neither doctor nor patient judged correctly:

A woman in her early sixties complained of severe pain in the hip due to osteoarthritis. She had been seen by an orthopaedic surgeon and was on the waiting list for hip replacement. Simple analgesics were having little effect and therefore it was decided to give her a trial of anti-inflammatory drugs pending surgery. She was warned about possible dyspeptic symptoms and asked to come back in a month to assess her response. The drug prescribed is one which is widely used and is regarded as reasonably safe. She came back a month later very ill indeed with signs of severe cardiac failure. She was breathless, with grossly swollen ankles, and deathly pale: a quick blood examination on the spot showed a haemoglobin level of about 25 per cent of normal. She had not noticed any dyspepsia but the drug had clearly caused slow bleeding from her gastro-intestinal tract and this anaemia had precipitated cardiac failure in an elderly but fit woman. She was referred to hospital as an emergency and fortunately responded to blood transfusion with concomitant treatment for her secondary cardiac failure.

A well-intentioned attempt to relieve this woman's severe but non-life threatening pain had come near to killing her. She had been warned only of indigestion so had ignored the other symptoms and because she 'had an appointment' she waited a full month before coming back. This is a slight inherent danger in an appointments system.

Further-reaching side-effects are illustrated by the following case:

A woman was referred through a national counselling agency. Seven years earlier her husband had planned to retire from work at 55 so that they could enjoy together their good health and comfortable pension. They had greatly looked forward to this, planning a move to the country and to explore Europe in their caravan. A few months before his retirement her husband had had a suspected mild heart attack which had entailed only a few days in hospital.

He had been reassured that it was not serious and had been put on some tablets which he was still taking. Unfortunately, his wife said, he had never really recovered. He went back to work till his 55th birthday but since this short illness had lost all his normal energy and enthusiasm for life: worst of all he had become impotent and as their physical marital relations had always been warm and a source of pleasure to them both this had caused great concern and perplexity. He was ashamed and embarrassed, refusing to discuss it, and they had gradually stopped making any demonstration of affection to each other. The new house in the country had been a disaster as he had neither the energy nor inclination to look after the garden and the caravan had been sold. She was bitterly disappointed at the way their later years had turned out after a very happy marriage and was almost suicidally depressed.

On tactful enquiry it was found that the 'heart tablets' the husband was taking were beta-blockers. The value of this group of drugs in coronary artery disease and hypertension is unquestioned, but, as they reduce cardiac work and output, a feeling of lethargy and fatigue is common: a direct side-effect in the male is impotence. This man had been taking the drug for many years for questionable therapeutic reasons: adjustment to retirement can be difficult in any case, but with this man, lethargy and particularly impotence had almost certainly led to secondary psychological effects which had virtually destroyed his retired life and a happy marriage.

Psychotropic drugs are of immense value in the treatment of psychiatric disease and many people with serious mental illness are able to live a reasonably normal life with the help of appropriate medication. Anti-depressants will probably shorten a temporary but unpleasant illness like post-influenzal depression but the following case illustrates what might go wrong through accident or misunderstanding on the part of either doctor or patient:

A man of 61 recently retired from work had become depressed after a bout of influenza and had been started by his doctor on a tricyclic anti-depressant. About a month later he moved to a different area and had to consult a new doctor about difficulty in emptying his bladder: as he had a moderately enlarged prostate he was referred to hospital for prostatectomy. This did not relieve his symptoms which depressed him further and his anti-depressants were increased. After about two years on this higher dose he was slow in speech and thought, overweight and an old man in every way. Fortunately he moved house again and his next doctor suspected that his sluggishness and urinary problems were due to over-medication with anti-depressant drugs. These were gradually reduced and eventually stopped: he lost weight and all his bladder problems and regained his previous physical and mental energy.

The following case is an example of an undesired direct-effect rather than side-effect.

A fit man in his mid-forties consulted his doctor on account of moderately severe tension symptoms associated with the pressure of his work. The problems were acknowledged and discussed but as it seemed impossible to resolve them in the near future he was given a long-acting beta-blocker to take daily to relieve the symptoms of stress. After a few months these symptoms had improved but he was disappointed to find that he had become easily fatigued and breathless on exertion: he had had to give up tennis and swimming which he had previously enjoyed and did not associate his diminished exercise tolerance with his 'tranquilliser'. Fortunately he reported these symptoms to his doctor who correctly interpreted them and persuaded him to discontinue his medication. His physical fitness quickly returned and he resolved to manage his stress by adjusting his work load, which was not as difficult as he had thought.

Beta-blockers represent a major breakthrough in the management of coronary artery disease and hypertension. They block nerve receptors in the heart muscle reducing its work and demand for oxygen. Severe anginal pain can be well controlled in this way but reduced cardiac output means a diminished response to exercise and the patient may be breathless on exertion and quickly tired. At the same time, and incidentally, they block other nerve receptors which trigger the body's response to nervous stress and they are much used by musicians for example as a single small dose before a performance. In these circumstances while not interfering with mental acuity and neuro-muscular function they prevent the bodily symptoms of acute short-lived stress such as palpitation, sweating and tremor. The last two can seriously interfere with playing a musical instrument and the occasional use of this category of drugs in such circumstances appears to be harmless and justifiable.

Historically, mankind has always looked for relief from stress, the oldest agent probably being alcohol. Opiates, barbiturates and more recently the benzodiazapenes have all had their vogue and been discarded because of their many drawbacks. Since the beta-blockers relieve stress *symptoms* without the danger of sedation or addiction they are being increasingly prescribed by some doctors for the relief of more general stress: the above case illustrates first the importance of weighing possible benefit against adverse effects, and secondly telling the patient what such adverse effects might be so that they can be recognised as such without delay.

The following case is an example of how mistaken clinical assessment coupled with unquestioned authoritarianism can cause very severe effects on a patient's life:

A man of 45 was in very good health but gave a history of a heart murmur which had been detected on routine examination while he was at school. On account of this his parents had been told that he must never be allowed to over-exert himself and they had conscientiously excluded him from all games and other strenuous activities. Fortunately he had been admitted to hospital at the age of 40 for minor surgery and the murmur had been noted by the anaesthetist who had referred him for cardiac assessment. Careful testing using modern techniques had indicated that the heart murmur had no serious significance whatsoever. Since then he had led a normal fully energetic life but had always regretted the forty years when the strenuous activities he so much enjoyed had been denied him.

Fortunately excessive medical authority is declining as patients become better educated and more articulate. The media deserve much credit in this area.

The greatest pharmacological advances which have been made in the treatment of both physical and mental illness are not to be decried: people are living longer and more comfortably because of them. This is sometimes denied by medical critics who see such claims as spurious and would relate all seeming advances in medicine to better social conditions and the natural attenuation of previously more virulent micro-organisms. Personally I find it difficult not to be impressed by a virtually overnight recovery from a serious condition like lobar pneumonia. Pharmacologically effective drugs almost invariably have side-effects, but if the disease is life-threatening, side-effects might simply have to be tolerated. When the situation is less clear-cut both doctor and patient must carefully weigh the expected advantages against the drawbacks. A steam roller should never be used to crack a nut.

Advice can be as damaging as drugs as the last example above showed and in this area the clergy have to be as careful as the doctors. Misguided spiritual advice or harsh judgement made of a penitent can cause, in a sensitive person, a drop in self-esteem from which he may never recover. Anxious people are acutely sensitive to tone of voice. Mistaken assessment of an isolated sinful act or a single personality weakness can cripple spiritually as the wrong interpretation of a single physical abnormality can cripple physically. The responsibility on the shoulders of those who deal with people in trouble is a heavy one: it is good that neither the doctor nor the priest is any longer regarded as God.

Endpiece

Many of the dilemmas in the foregoing pages have resulted from comparatively recent medical advances each of which has raised a new set of moral problems to which there is no ready answer. The Christian doctor therefore must often be prepared to carry the cross of uncertainty when trying to balance the claims of his patient's needs against those arising from his concept of traditional Christian moral norms, and, in the case of the Catholic doctor, against the specific teaching of the Magisterium of the Church.

Until the introduction of the sulphonamides for instance, in the mid-1930s and the antibiotics a few years later there was no question about whether an old person should be allowed to die from broncho-pneumonia; they simply died. All babies with spina bifida quickly succumbed to meningitis; now, however, assessment for suitability for operation is necessary, painful and difficult for both surgeon and parents. The severest degrees can be diagnosed ante-natally and may constitute legal grounds for termination of pregnancy.

In the last 15 years we have seen the development of the transplantation of kidney and more recently of single vital organs such as liver and heart. Intensive care techniques enable a patient with severe brain damage to be kept alive for long periods sometimes leading to near miraculous recovery, but often to the difficult decision to discontinue the life-support system when brain injury is clearly irreversible. When such a decision is taken, should the overriding consideration be for the patient and his family or for the needs of others depending for survival on transplantation of his organs? Given time to find suitable tissue-matching recipients four lives might be saved from reception of his heart, liver and each of his kidneys.

Contraception has been with us for centuries: primitive contraceptive devices have been found on archaeological sites and there are few household substances which have not been tried as spermicides at one time or another. It is only in our time that the doctor has become involved and success virtually guaranteed.

Attempts to terminate pregnancy have also been a common feature in human history, attested by the many ecclesiastic, philosophic and legal pronouncements on the subject. Such attempts were usually made by the woman herself or by an amateur more or less skilled in the matter and were forbidden not only by the church but by the law. Now however, the law permits termination in a wide variety of circumstances. The procedures are becoming increasingly refined and are carried out in hospital by qualified members of the medical profession whose own code of ethics in the matter closely reflects not only the law but the International Code of Medical Ethics as formulated in the Declaration of Oslo in 1970.

In the fields of infertility and genetics particularly rapid and controversial advances are being made. While it is true that the fact that something can be done does not necessarily mean that it should be done, the benefit to infertile couples and to those with a family history of grave congenital disorder is beyond dispute.

It is right and ever more necessary that the Christian churches should concern themselves with matters relating to science and the welfare of the human race and that moral questions should be illuminated by theological insights.

It is the *particularity* of the pronouncements of the Catholic Church which has caused and is continuing to cause such widespread concern. It is hard, in 1989, to believe that the churches (including the Catholic Church) once opposed, on *moral* grounds, anaesthesia for a woman in labour: it may be that in the next century it will seem similarly incredible that the Catholic Church in our time should have prohibited the contraceptive pill.

My concern in addressing these questions as a Catholic doctor and in trying to share with readers my views born of medical experience springs from a deep love and central loyalty to the Church coupled with the fear that its image and true significance is becoming discredited by inappropriate pronouncements on matters which are regarded by many as peripheral to Christian conviction and affirmation.

Notes

Biblical quotations throughout the text are from the Revised Standard Version.

Chapter I: Reflections on Authority

1. W. M. Abbott (ed.) (1967) *The Documents of Vatican II*, Geoffrey Chapman, London, 'Dignitatis Humanae', par. 3, p. 680.
2. Ibid., 'Gaudium et Spes', par. 16, p. 213.
3. Ibid., 'Gaudium et Spes', par. 62, p. 270.
4. John Habgood (1980) *A Working Faith*, Darton, Longman & Todd, London, p. 112.
5. John Mahoney (1987) *The Making of Moral Theology*, Oxford University Press, Oxford, p. 134.
6. Habgood, *A Working Faith*, p. 114.

Chapter II: Some Reflections on Suffering

1. John Hick (1966) *Evil and the God of Love*, Macmillan, London.
2. Daniel Berrigan (1973) *America is Hard to Find*, SPCK, London.
3. Helen Waddell (1933) *Peter Abelard*, Constable, London, Book IV 'The Paraclete'.
4. Carl Rogers (1961) *On Becoming A Person*, Houghton-Mifflin, Boston, Mass., pp. 39–44.
5. Robert Runcie, *et al.* (1986) *Encounters: Exploring Christian Faith*, Darton, Longman & Todd, London, p. 9.

Chapter III: Contraception

1. John Mahoney (1986) 'A Flawed Giant', *The Tablet*, 10 May. Mahoney is here citing Augustine's *City of God*.
2. Jack Dominion (1978) *Sexual Integrity*, Darton, Longman & Todd, London, p. 39.
3. Ibid., p. 72ff.

Chapter IV: Sterilisation

1. J. K. Mason and R. A. McCall Smith (1987) *Law and Medical Ethics*, 2nd Edition, Butterworth, London, p. 69. The authors cite the 'Jeannette' case in clarifying the legal situation of a minor referred for sterilisation.

Chapter V: The Status of the Embryo

1. The Sacred Congregation for the Doctrine of the Faith (1974) *Declaration on Abortion*, para. 1471.
2. Bernard Häring (1974) *Medical Ethics*, Revised Edition, St Paul Publications, Langley, pp. 99ff.
3. John Mahoney (1987) *The Making of Moral Theology*, Oxford University Press, Oxford, p. 9.
4. Häring, *Medical Ethics*, pp. 100, 101.
5. Kenneth Boyd, Brendan Callaghan, Edward Shotter (1986) *Life Before Birth: Consensus in Medical Ethics*, SPCK, London, p. 21. The authors cite *Abortion: an Ethical Discussion* (1965), Church Information Office, London.
6. Ibid., p. 23. The authors cite General Synod (1979) *Report of Proceedings*, Vol. 10, No. 3, p. 1158, November, Church Information Office, London.
7. Ibid., p. 28. The authors cite General Assembly of the Church of Scotland (1966) *Social and Moral Welfare Report*.
8. Teilhard de Chardin (1959) *The Phenomenon of Man*, Collins, Glasgow.
9. Häring, *Medical Ethics*, pp. 83–84.

10. Herbert McCabe, *God Matters* (1987) Geoffrey Chapman, London, pp. 111, 118.
11. Edward Schillebeeckx (1977) *The Eucharist*, 2nd Edition, Sheed & Ward, London, p. 100.

Chapter VI: Abortion

1. Alastair Campbell (1984) *Moral Dilemmas in Medicine*, 3rd Edition, Churchill Livingstone, London, p. 126.
2. The Sacred Congregation for the Doctrine of the Faith (1987) *Instruction in respect of Human Life and the Dignity of Procreation*, Sec. 1, para. 2.
3. J. K. Mason and R. A. McCall Smith (1987) *Law and Medical Ethics*, 2nd Edition, Butterworth, London, p. 83.
4. Ibid., p. 83.
5. Ibid., p. 69.

Chapter VII: Infertility

1. Kenneth Boyd, Brendan Callaghan, Edward Shotter (1986) *Life before Birth: Consensus in Medical Ethics*, SPCK, London, p. 81. The authors cite *Artificial Human Insemination* (1948) (report of the Archbishop of Canterbury's Commission).
2. Ibid., pp. 87–88.
3. The Sacred Congregation for the Doctrine of the Faith (1987) *Instruction in Respect of Human Life in its Origin and the Dignity of Procreation*, Part 2: 'Interventions upon Human Procreation'.
4. Boyd, Callaghan, Shotter (1986) *Life before Birth*, p. 96. The authors cite CIS (1983d), p. 10.
5. Ibid., p. 101.
6. Ibid., p. 103.
7. The Sacred Congregation for the Doctrine of the Faith (1987) *Instruction in Respect of Human Life in its Origin and the Dignity of Procreation*, Part 2: 'Is homologous IVF Morally Licit?'

8. Boyd, Callaghan, Shotter (1986) *Life before Birth*, p. 96. The authors cite CIS (1983d), p. 10.

9. Suggested to the author in a personal communication (1988) by J. P. J. Jansen, Leidsherdam, The Netherlands.

10. J. K. Mason and R. A. McCall Smith (1987) *Law and Medical Ethics*, 2nd Edition, Butterworth, London, p. 45.

11. Boyd, Callaghan, Shotter (1986) *Life before Birth* Church of England (1984), p. 7f.

12. Ibid., p. 102.

13. Brother Lawrence of the Resurrection (17th century) *The Practice of the Presence of God* (Translated by John J. Delaney), Image Books (Doubleday & Company, Inc.), Garden City, New York, Second Conversation, 28 September 1666, p. 43.

14. Mason and McCall Smith (1987) *Law and Medical Ethics*, p. 45.

15. Boyd, Callaghan, Shotter (1986) *Life before Birth*, p. 88. The authors cite CIS (1983c), p. 8.

16. Ibid., p. 92. The authors cite Church of Scotland (1985) *Reports to the General Assembly, Board for Social Responsibility*, p. 290.

17. Ibid., p. 90. The authors cite *Choices in Childlessness* (1982) Free Church Federal Council/British Council of Churches, London, p. 45.

18. W. J. Winslade (1981) 'Private Right or Public Wrong?', *Journal of Medical Ethics*.

Chapter VIII: Homosexuality and AIDS

1. Bernard Häring (1974) *Medical Ethics*, Revised Edition, St Paul Publications, Langley, p. 185.

Chapter IX: Death and Dying

1. Bernard Häring (1975) *Manipulation*, St Paul Publications, Langley, p. 106.

2. J. K. Mason and R. A. McCall Smith (1987) *Law and*

Medical Ethics, 2nd Edition, Butterworth, London, pp. 105–106.
3. Ivan Illich (1975) *Medical Nemesis*, Calder & Boyars, London, pp. 40–41.

Chapter X: Transplant Surgery

1. J. K. Mason and R. A. McCall Smith (1987) *Law and Medical Ethics*, 2nd Edition, Butterworth, London, p. 228.
2. Bernard Häring (1974) *Medical Ethics*, Revised Edition, St Paul Publications, Langley, p. 138. Häring is here citing, Charles Dubost (1969) 'Scientific and Ethical Problems in Organ Transplantation', *The Annals of Thoracic Surgery*, August, p. 102.

Chapter XI: The Harm We Do

1. Alastair V. Campbell (1984) *Moderated Love: A Theology of Pastoral Care*, SPCK, London, p. 26. Campbell is here quoting, Anna Sexton (1975) 'Doctors' in *The Awful Rowing Towards God*, Houghton-Mifflin, Boston, Mass., pp. 74f.